ALIYA

ALIYA

Stories of the Elephants of Sri Lanka

Teresa Cannon and Peter Davis

Foreword by Dr Arthur C. Clarke

AIRAVATA PRESS

MELBOURNE

Aliya

Stories of the Elephants of Sri Lanka

Teresa Cannon and Peter Davis

Foreword by Dr Arthur C. Clarke

Airavata Press

Published by Airavata Press

PO Box 204

Ferntree Gully

Victoria 3156

Australia

Facsimile +61 3 97522027

Distributed by

Blue Dolphin Publishing, Inc.

P.O. Box 8

Nevada City, CA 95959 USA

North, South, and Central America

Great Britain, Europe, and South Africa

Orders: 1-800-643-0765

Editor: Veronica James

Design & layout: Harry Kontos and Jo Sullivan with Teresa Cannon

Photography: Peter Davis and Teresa Cannon

Additional photography: Patrick Horton (p. 127); Rex Seilman (p. 165)

Typeset in ITC Garamond Condensed, Monotype Castellar and Linotype Snell Roundhand

Printed and bound in Singapore by Tien Wah Press

Painting: *Mythology* Hiltrud Barfus (pp. 8-9)

Painting: *Panamure Kraal* Dr P.E.P. Deraniyagala (p. 93)

Permission to reproduce excerpts from *Loris* granted by Dr Ranjen Fernando

Permission for use of material from Colombo Museum Library granted by Dr Thelma Gunawardene

Permission to reproduce envelope and stamp of Raja granted by Mr H. Kumarasinghe

Permission to reproduce painting *Panamure Kraal* granted by Dr S.U. Deraniyagala

National Library of Australia Cataloguing–in–Publication data:

Cannon, Teresa

Aliya : Stories of the Elephants of Sri Lanka

Bibliography.

Includes index.

ISBN 0 646 21408 X

1. Elephants – Sri Lanka I. Davis, Peter

II. Title

599.61095493

Front cover: The Venerable B. Wimalaratana, Rajamaha Viharaya, Bellanwila, with temple elephant, Chandru.

We dedicate this book to peace in Sri Lanka

The elephant headed god, Ganesha, draws millions of devotees from around the world. Among other things he is honoured as Lord of Beginnings, Lord of Obstacles and Lord of Writing. At the beginning of any major undertaking his devotees pay tribute. This is especially so at the beginning of a book. With respect for this tradition we acknowledge the qualities symbolised by this deity – among them, clarity of purpose, understanding, wisdom and, pertinent to all of these, humour.

FOREWORD

In 1956, I settled in Sri Lanka, a perfect place from which to view the vastness of the universe and explore the depths of the ocean. It is also an idyllic location to marvel at one of the most remarkable creatures that walk the earth – the elephant.

In ancient mythology, elephants held up the universe. To this day, they continue to play a crucial role in the culture and ceremonies of this island nation. Yet the very survival of these majestic creatures is threatened today. Experts predict that the Sri Lankan elephant, a unique subspecies of the Asian elephant, may soon disappear in the wild, unless major conservation measures are undertaken.

In view of this, it is timely that a well-researched book on the Sri Lankan elephant has been compiled by Peter Davis and Teresa Cannon. I first met the authors after they had completed their initial field trip, and we talked with enthusiasm about the exceptional attributes of elephants. I knew that I had met two obsessed people, who had embarked on a journey to research, photograph and write about the creatures that touched them so deeply. I cautioned them about the long road ahead, and am delighted that they have made the distance.

The authors have created an interesting and valuable documentation of Sri Lankan elephants. It combines aspects of elephant history, mythology and behaviour with many touching anecdotes. I am particularly happy to note that the book features the Elephant Orphanage at Pinnawala – that enchanting place which no visitor to Sri Lanka should miss.

This beautifully illustrated book fills an important gap not only in the literature on Sri Lanka but also on the accessible writing on the Asian elephant. Books cannot save elephants or other animals. But they can – and do – enhance popular awareness about conservation issues and needs.

I am happy to commend *Aliya – Stories of the Elephants of Sri Lanka* to anyone who cares about these gentle giants.

Arthur C. Clarke, CBE

Chancellor, University of Moratuwa, Sri Lanka

Chancellor, International Space University

Colombo, Sri Lanka

25 June, 1994

CONTENTS

CONTENTS

ACKNOWLEDGEMENTS

The publication of *Aliya – Stories of the Elephants of Sri Lanka* has many similarities to the arrival of a newborn elephant. The gestation of an elephant is a lengthy process. And just as a baby elephant is supported by many in the herd, so the birth of this book has received much nurturing and support.

Throughout the four years of research, writing and photography we received generous assistance across four continents from numerous individuals and organisations. We thank all of you and we sincerely hope that through your assistance, *Aliya* will foster a broader understanding and appreciation of the elephants in Sri Lanka. We are particularly indebted to the following people and organisations who sponsored our work from the very beginning:

Airlanka

Mr Cyril Gardiner, Chairman, Galle Face Hotel

Management and staff of Galle Face Hotel

The Ceylon Tourist Board

AGFA-Gevaert, Australia

We have subtitled our book *Stories of the Elephants of Sri Lanka*. Many of our stories involve people. And many of the people we have encountered are themselves worthy of a story. It would be impossible to mention all those who rendered assistance along the way. We are grateful to all who supported the project and in particular the following people:

The staff at **Airlanka** in Melbourne, Sydney and Colombo were always encouraging. We especially thank **Mr Chan Wicks, Mr Rienzi Pereira** and **Ms Manju Jacobs**. With the help of **American Airlines** we were able to put faces (and trunks) to names in Los Angeles, New York and Washington. The **Venerable Olande Ananda** was one of the first people to assist us. He offered valuable information. He translated the words of his teacher, the **Venerable Davuldena Nanissara Thero**. This revered High Priest delighted us with his stories of the Buddha and elephants. Throughout our work we have returned many times to his ideas and words of advice. In his quiet and singular way, **Mr W.M. Bandara**, Curator of the Pinnawala Elephant Orphanage, welcomed us many times. We were touched by his concern for the elephants in his care. With his co-operation and assistance we were able to observe and learn much about elephants. In spite of his busy schedule organising temple festivities, **Mr Bandaranayake**, Private Secretary, Temple of the Sacred Tooth Relic, always found time to answer our questions in his own profound and humorous style. **Ms Hiltrud Barfus** became almost as obsessed as we were and responded enthusiastically to our request for a painting on the mythology of the elephants. **Mr Roger A. Caras**, President of the American Society for Prevention of Cruelty to Animals, wrote letters of support and encouragement. The staff at the **Ceylon Tourist Board** assisted us with information and transport. **Dr Arthur C. Clarke** always found time to talk about elephants, and whales, and sharks, and almost any other creature of our universe or indeed any other universe. We are especially grateful for his support and we feel privileged that he has written the foreword to this book. On a hot and dusty afternoon in Galle **Mr Wijayananda Dahanayake**, former Prime Minister, and his nephew **Mr Vijaya Dahanayake** told us stories of elephants and how to live a long life by following the Buddhist path. Along a car-choked dusty road in Kandy, **Ms Veena De Silva's** tiny bookshop houses many treasures. We are grateful for her assistance with our obscure requests. **Mr Jayantha De Silva** allowed us to spend valuable time with his treasured elephant, the retired Baby Nona. **Mr Howard Debenham**, Australian High Commissioner for Sri Lanka, gave us much needed support and reassurance. When the going got tough his diplomacy and damage control eased the way. At the Los Angeles Zoo, Curator of Mammals, **Mr Michael Dee** had many treasures for us – his enthusiasm, his creative ideas on elephants and zoos, and a copy of the ancient book on elephant lore, the *Hastividyarnava*. In our conversations with **Dr Siran Deraniyagala**, son of the legendary elephant expert Dr P.E.P. Deraniyagala, we learnt much about elephants and Sri Lanka. We are also indebted to him for permission to reproduce his father's painting of the Panamure Kraal (1944). **Ms Valerie Eckanayake** offered creative suggestions, extraordinary contacts and unlimited hospitality. She steered us along some amazing paths. We enjoyed and were reassured by the straightforward manner of **Mr Hector Eckanayake**. We arrived at the home of **Mr Sam Elapata** with police convoy. His captivating elephant experiences and extensive library broadened the picture of our project. **Dr Ranjen Fernando**, Director, Wildlife and Nature Protection Society of Sri Lanka, expressed thoughtful support. We are grateful for his permission to use excerpts from the Society's magazine, *Loris*. **Mr Bradley Fernando**, former Director, Zoological Gardens in Colombo, exuded the inspiring presence of one who respects and knows elephants. His firm commitment to our project was most welcome. Our part-time neighbours **Padmini and John Frawley** maintained a regular supply of newspaper clippings and excellent Sri Lankan food. **The Venerable Gala Boda Gnanissara**, Chief Priest, Gangaramaya Temple in Colombo, had no objection to our unannounced arrival. His boundless energy led us to many elephants and elephant people. **Mr Cyril Gardiner**, Chairman of the famous Galle Face Hotel in Colombo, has inspired us with his inimitable manner and contagious humour. His support for and interest in our work never waned. In our sometimes frenetic state, the **Staff of the Galle Face Hotel** presented to us another pace and style. They made us feel like part of the family. **Ms Bev Googe** of AGFA-Gevaert in Melbourne, generously assisted with film and processing. The painstaking efforts of **Dr Brendon Gooneratne** greatly strengthened our manuscript. Dr Gooneratne is a medical practitioner, historian, art collector, lover of elephants and head of Project Jonah in Australia. His attention to detail and his constructive comments were particularly welcome. We are grateful to **Dr Thelma Gunawardene**, Director, National Museums, who gave us access to rare manuscripts and permission to reproduce excerpts. When we met **Mr and Mrs Gunasekara** in Kandy we knew we were in the company of people who respect elephants. The short time we spent with them and their elephant Raja remains precious. We appreciate very much the co-operation of both **Mr E.L.B. Hurulle** and **Mr N. Wijesundera**, former Sri Lankan High Commissioners to Australia. **Ms Veronica James** was more than an editor. From the moment of her involvement she became a committed third party. Her reassurance and creativity buoyed us through the final stages. We enjoyed intensive collaboration with **Mr Harry Kontos** and **Ms Jo Sullivan**, designers of *Aliya*. When we accompanied veterinarian, **Dr D.S. Kodikara** on his regular round of treating sick elephants, we gained a unique insight into a crucial part of Sri Lankan life. In his quiet and thoughtful way **Dr Sarath Kotagama**, former Director, Department of Wildlife Conservation, helped us fill many of the gaps. **Mr H. Kumarasinghe**, Director, Philatelic Bureau, Colombo, graciously granted us permission to reproduce the envelope and stamp of Raja, the revered Temple Tusker. **Dr Vijitha Kuruwita**, Head of Veterinary Studies, University of Peradeniya, Kandy, generously provided information about Raja, as well as details on treatments and tranquillising of elephants. On a freezing day at the Washington Zoological Park, **Mr John Lehnhardt**, Collection Manager and **Ms Marie Galloway**, Elephant Keeper, made us warmly welcome. With their co-operation we met and photographed Shanthi, the Sri Lankan elephant in their care and Kumari, Shanthi's five week old baby. **Mr Ajit Lokuge** spoke to us of frogs, bromeliads and analogue forestry. Such ideas may protect an environment where people and elephants may live in peace. The printing of this book is due to the thoughtfulness of **Ms Geneve Maier** who patiently counselled us on the labyrinthine intricacies of the print process. In Melbourne, **Mr Victor Melder** generously supplied us with many useful texts and photocopies from his vast collection of Sri Lankan literature. **Mr R. Mottau** saved us from yet another fruitless journey in our search for the burial site of Major Thomas Rogers. He took us there directly. From walls of shoe boxes in his home, this 90 year old retired Colombo archivist extracted references for our research. At Kataragama we spent many pleasurable hours with **Mr S. Nagaraja** who guided and informed us about the nuances and complexities of the sanctuary and the temples within. From the Pali Text Society in London, **Ms Sally Mellick** dispatched much needed material with speed and efficiency. At Pelwatte Sugar Company, **Mr Terry Pearse,** Agricultural Manager, and **Mr Rex Seilman**, Manager, Elephant Control Unit, enabled us to further our understanding of the dilemmas confronting human/elephant interaction. Through their co-operation we witnessed the pocketed herd at Handapanagala. We are indebted to **Brothers Peter** and **Justin** from the Community of the Many Names of God, Llanpumsaint in Wales. They generously supplied materials about their elephant, Valli. **Mr J.P.I. (Hemantha) Piyasiri** generously included us in his visits to his elephants. He gave us insight into a more contemporary way of elephants and their owners. In Melbourne **Mr Brian Potts** gave generously of his time to produce quality images of the painting depicting the mythology. To the late **President Premadasa** we are grateful for his expressions of support. We regret that like some others who supported this project, he is not alive to see its fruition. **Madame Premadasa**, former First Lady, showed us hospitality and introduced us to the work of her son **Mr Sajith Premadasa**, who shared with us his ideas about the tusked elephants he so much admires. With support and customary fine service, **Qantas Airways** enabled us to further our research beyond Australian shores. **Professor W.D. Ratnasooriya**, University of Colombo, willingly offered us his research findings which have provided a basis for wider knowledge of the elephant, particularly in regard to breeding. We were distressed and saddened to hear of the death of **Mr Sam Samarasinghe**, who had a vast knowledge and love of elephants. We are deeply indebted to **Mrs Carmine Samarasinghe** who maintained contact, providing us with invaluable information especially in regard to her little elephant, Puja. Within the stifling heat and antiquated walls of the library at the Lake House Messrs **R. Senadheere** and **D.J.S. de Silva**, Associated Newspapers of Ceylon, made press clippings on elephants materialise and coaxed the photocopier until it churned out the required articles. **Dr Ranil Senanayake** preached to us the virtues of soil management, the abundance of frogs and the importance of listening for the sound of the bird which heralds the long-awaited monsoon. **Mr Saman Senanayake** added substantially to our elephant knowledge by introducing the former rogue, Sankha. **Dr Jeheskel Shoshani** and **Ms Sandra Shoshani**, Elephant Research Foundation, Michigan, have shown considerable support and interest throughout our project. To Sandra we are particularly grateful for her creative ideas, contacts and materials. To Jeheskel, amongst many things, we are indebted for the 'customised' tour of the Museum of Natural History in New York. This wonderfully outrageous journey led us through the darkened bowels where million year old fossils crouch spectre-like along creaking benches. **Mr K.D. Sumanabanda** evokes many happy memories – vivacious greetings, the splendid traditions of the mahout, the sacredness in which he holds the elephant, his humility and sincerity. In his quiet unassuming way, **Matara Swami** sat with us in the grounds of the Kataragama Shrines talking of the jungle people and their ways with elephants. **Mr and Mrs Thadhani** displayed with pride their elephant dresses. They spoke of measurements and amounts, Thai silks and velvets and their contribution to ancient traditions. Initially **Mr A. Thangavel**, Secretary, Sri Selva Vinayagar Temple, Kandy, was disturbed at our untimely arrival. But he quickly relented and welcomed us warmly after learning the reasons for our visit. We appreciated his openness, his stories and his generous assistance. After three years of faxes into cyberspace, we finally had the privilege of meeting **Mr Neranjan Wijeratne**, Lay Custodian to the Temple of the Sacred Tooth Relic. He shared with us his memories of Raja, the revered temple tusked elephant, as well as many stories of *peraheras* (festive processions), Sri Lankan customs and temple traditions. During the Colombo *perahera*, **Elephant Wilbert** gave us a valuable insight into traditional medicines and treatments for elephants. The **Venerable B. Wimalaratana**, Rajamaha Viharaya, Bellanwila, graciously escorted us to meet his temple elephant Chandru. We are deeply indebted to him for his permission to take photographs and particularly to use the image on the cover of this book.

To our families and all our friends – a big thankyou for staying with us.

And finally, we acknowledge Anusha, Baby Nona, Sankha, Bibile, Valli, Shanthi, Kumari, Lakshmi, Menika, Chandru, Vijaya, Sukamali, the many Rajas and all the elephants of Sri Lanka we were privileged to encounter – and those we did not meet.

CHRONOLOGY OF EVENTS

546 BC	Sinhalese arrive on island of Sri Lanka
377 BC	City of Anuradhapura established
306 BC	Buddhism introduced to Sri Lanka
289 BC	Arrival of bo-tree
205 BC	Elara began reign in Anuradhapura
161–137 BC	Reign of King Dutugemunu
161 BC	Elara defeated by Dutugemunu and his elephant Kandula
120 BC	Construction of the great Thupa, Ruwanweli, began
301 AD	Arrival of the Tooth Relic of the Buddha
1505	Arrival of the Portuguese
1597	Beginning of Portuguese rule
1656	Beginning of Dutch rule
1796	Beginning of British rule
1832	Sri Wickrema Rajasinghe, last king of Kandy, died
1837	First sugar plantation in Ceylon established
1844	Slavery abolished
1845	Appointment of Sir James Emerson Tennent as Colonial Secretary. Two years later appointed as Lieutenant Governor
1845	Death of Major Thomas William Rogers, Assistant Government Agent and elephant hunter
1847	Sacred Tooth Relic of the Buddha handed back by the British to the priests and chieftains of Kandy. Six years later placed in the care of the high priests and custodian of the Sacred Tooth Temple
1883	First sales of Ceylon teas
1900	Birth of Dr P.E.P Deraniyagala
1948	Ceylon became an independent nation
1950	Last elephant kraal held in Ceylon at Panamure
1951	Death of Sir Francis Molamure, First Parliamentary Speaker and organiser of the last elephant kraal
1988	Death of Raja, the elephant which had carried the relics of the Buddha in procession for almost 50 years

INTRODUCTION

*Of all footprints,
that of the elephant is supreme…*

BUDDHA

To thee I give, dear Kandula

the Lordship over the whole island of Lanka.

WITH these words, in 161 BC[1], the Lankan King Dutugemunu, honoured his elephant, Kandula.[2] With this book we wish to honour and celebrate all elephants of Lanka, known today as Sri Lanka. From our first visit we became transfixed by the majesty and serenity of the elephants that walk the island. Our imagining has been fuelled by the very fact that the world's largest land mammal survives on such a beautiful yet tiny and crowded place.

As we began our research so the stories unfolded. At the festivals and ceremonies we touched ancient traditions. In the modest homes of those who work with elephants and in the palatial dwellings of those who own elephants, the tapestry of story-telling gathered momentum. In the libraries and archives we filled in the gaps.

But it was in the jungles and parks where the dwindling numbers of wild elephants roam, that we glimpsed the story of the future. It was there we experienced a sense of urgency that comes with knowing that what you see is destined to vanish.

To engage the eyes of these elephants is to feel both pleasure and pain; pleasure because they remind us of qualities we admire – loyalty, strength, dignity and intelligence; pain because we know that these creatures which walked the earth long before humans, may well disappear within our lifetime.

The plight of these elephants is of our own making. If we allow them to disappear, we are allowing part of us to vanish as well. It is that part of us that believes the earth is for all creatures to share. To deny this is to sacrifice our imagining.

SETTING THE SCENE

SRI LANKA, formerly Ceylon, is a tiny island with a land mass of just over 65,000 square kilometres. It is smaller than Tasmania. It is half the size of New York State. And it is only a quarter of the area of the United Kingdom. Yet its population of 17 million is equal to that of Australia.

Approximately 70 per cent of the population is Buddhist, 20 per cent Hindu and the rest are Muslim and Christian. The spiritual and cultural traditions of the island represent a fascinating and often complex blend of ancient and contemporary rituals.

Elephants have always been integral to the island. To this day they are prominent in religious and civil ceremonies. They carry sacred relics in colourful processions, their image adorns numerous temples and they are said to bring good fortune to those who cross their path.

Exactly how elephants came to the island is a matter of some debate. Some claim that the creatures evolved on the island. Others state that the elephants came across from India. Whatever the case, over the millennia, the Sri Lankan elephants developed into a unique subspecies of the Asian elephant, and are known as *Elephas maximus maximus*.

Throughout history the Sri Lankan elephants have been particularly prized for their strength and intelligence. For over 2,000 years they have been captured, tamed and employed for sport and for battle. Many were exported to distant lands. During the waves of colonial rule from the 16th century, wild elephants were captured in ever-increasing numbers. Many hundreds were employed to clear the land for plantations, construct railways and carve roads for the infrastructure of what is modern Sri Lanka. It was also during this period that elephants were slaughtered in their thousands by sportsmen seeking either an easy thrill or a government reward for 'eradicating vermin'.

Today there are an estimated 2,000 to 3,000 wild elephants living in the parks and jungles of Sri Lanka. That there is even one wild elephant remaining is perhaps a credit to conservationists and those involved with wildlife management. The population of domestic elephants is estimated at around 500.

This book is not a scientific and academic treatise. There are many such books. Rather our intention is to capture and reveal the essence of the elephant particularly within the rich culture that is Sri Lanka. We offer insights into their history and mythology, facts and figures as well as many personal stories of particular elephants and our experiences with them.

On Animals and Humans

A note on the origins and the species: There is much debate about the classification of the Sri Lankan elephant. Some claim that several distinct subspecies exist, all unique to Sri Lanka. Others claim that whilst there are different groupings of elephants, these have evolved from the varying geographical and climatic conditions on the island. The debate is confused by the fact that elephants have also been imported from other Asian countries.[3]

We do not challenge these views. We celebrate all the elephants of Sri Lanka no matter how they are categorised.

A note on anthropomorphism: Most people who encounter elephants are moved by their size and behaviour. We too have been moved. In describing them we have endeavoured to avoid excessive anthropomorphism.

Language however has been designed and developed by the human mind. It is only through language, through this human invention that we can communicate, and describe creatures such as elephants.

We trust that in being moved by the elephants and in recounting our wonderment, we have not veered too close to the anthropomorphic edge. Sometimes language seems so inadequate.

SRI LANKA

Jaffna

BAY OF BENGAL

Trincomalee

Wilpattu
National
Park

Anuradhapura

Mihintale

INDIAN OCEAN

Polonnaruwa

Batticaloa

Kurunegala

Kandy

Pinnawala
Elephant
Orphanage

Kegalle

Bibile

Kelaniya

Nuwara Eliya

Badulla

COLOMBO

Sri Pada
Adam's Peak

Haputale

Pelwatte

Ratnapura

Yala
National
Park

Kataragama
Kataragama Peak

Katagamuwa

Bundala

Galle

INDIAN OCEAN

ONE

FROM
ANCIENT
TIMES

From the Cosmic Egg

From the depths of the Celestial Ocean

Elephants emerged into the Universe

ELEPHANTS IN MYTHOLOGY

Like the entwining and caressing of elephant trunks,
The myths of the elephants have woven their way
Through societies and cultures,
Creating a rich labyrinth of legends,
Gently informing,
Quietly imprinting,
A profound knowing of the unknowable.

MYTHS are powerful and insightful clues into the essence of a culture. They link the past to the present, and give substance to belief and practice. Mythology expresses the inexpressible. To glimpse the myths of the elephants is to discover a rich tapestry which ascribes meaning and significance to the elephant. The threads of this tapestry continue to permeate the psyches and practices of many cultures. Mythology assigns elephants a profound place in creation, one that is akin to the divine, to the sacred. In mythology, elephants are associated with the rare, with the precious. They are the life source.

The early elephant mythologies grew from civilisations in the Middle East and the Indus Valley. As people migrated, so too did their myths and beliefs. As new civilisations evolved, new myths emerged.

In Sri Lanka today, many myths, although not immediately apparent, lie just beneath the surface, continuing to influence a more contemporary culture.

From the Cosmic Egg

One of the early legends on the origins of the elephants is told in the Sanskrit text *Matangalila (The Playful Treatise on Elephants)*.

According to this legend:

Brahma the Creator, took the Cosmic Egg *(Hiranyagarbha)* into his hands. It was from the *Hiranyagarbha*, that the sun had been born. And from this same Cosmic Egg, Garuda the golden mythical creature, of human and bird appearance, had burst forth in a radiant brilliance. Holding the two halves of the egg, one in each hand, Brahma breathed on them and chanted *Saman* (seven holy melodies). Within the essence of this ritual, Airavata, the cosmic white elephant emerged from the shell in his right hand. Seven male elephants followed. From the shell in Brahma's left hand, Abhramu and seven female elephants emerged. These 16 original elephants formed eight pairs and are the ancestors of all elephants, the elephants of heaven and of earth. They became the foundations of the earth, holding positions at the four main compass points and the intervening points. They are known as the *dig-gajas,* that is the elephants of the directions of space.[4]

Within each animal, Brahma placed a secret, sacred mystery.

Within the elephant he concealed wisdom.[5]

The Dig-gajas
UNIVERSAL POSITIONS OF THE MYTHICAL ELEPHANTS [6]

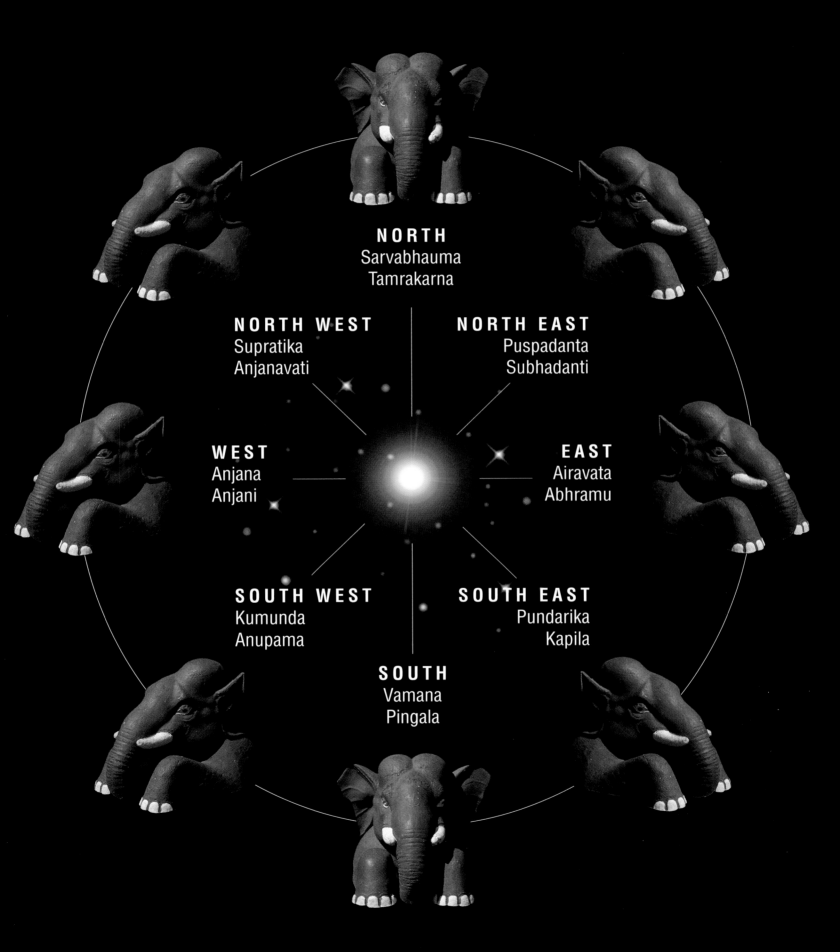

NORTH
Sarvabhauma
Tamrakarna

NORTH WEST
Supratika
Anjanavati

NORTH EAST
Puspadanta
Subhadanti

WEST
Anjana
Anjani

EAST
Airavata
Abhramu

SOUTH WEST
Kumunda
Anupama

SOUTH EAST
Pundarika
Kapila

SOUTH
Vamana
Pingala

How the Elephants Lost Their Wings

In the ancient text on the science of elephants, the *Gaja Sastra* (600–500 BC), it is told:

Initially elephants had wings. They moved through the heavens floating freely as clouds, or maybe flying with purpose, at times descending to stroll on earth. One day several elephants landed on a tree above the sage, named Dirghatapas (Long Austerity), who was tutoring his students. The weight of the elephants was too much for the branch of the tree. It snapped and broke. The elephants unperturbed calmly took another perch. Meanwhile the branch fell to earth killing some of the students. The sage, furious at this indiscreet behaviour, placed a curse on all elephants.

In future they would:

† Be wingless and condemned to walk the earth

† Forfeit their divine power

† Be subjected to human beings and be the vehicles for kings and nobles

† Have two tusks instead of four

† Lose knowledge of their own might

† Play with dust

† Burn with fire inside their stomachs

† Perspire within their bodies[7]

The *dig-gajas*, those elephants stationed at the cardinal points were not cursed. They appealed to Brahma on behalf of their descendants. They were concerned that their kin, unused to earthly conditions, may be vulnerable to the afflictions and diseases of earth. Moved at their trepidation for their relations, Brahma assured the *dig-gajas* that in time he would send to earth a sage, knowledgable in elephant lore and wellbeing. In this way Brahma would guarantee the earthly elephants health, safety and longevity. Satisfied with Brahma's promise, the *dig-gajas* returned to their respective positions at the cardinal points. Their offspring descended to earth.[8]

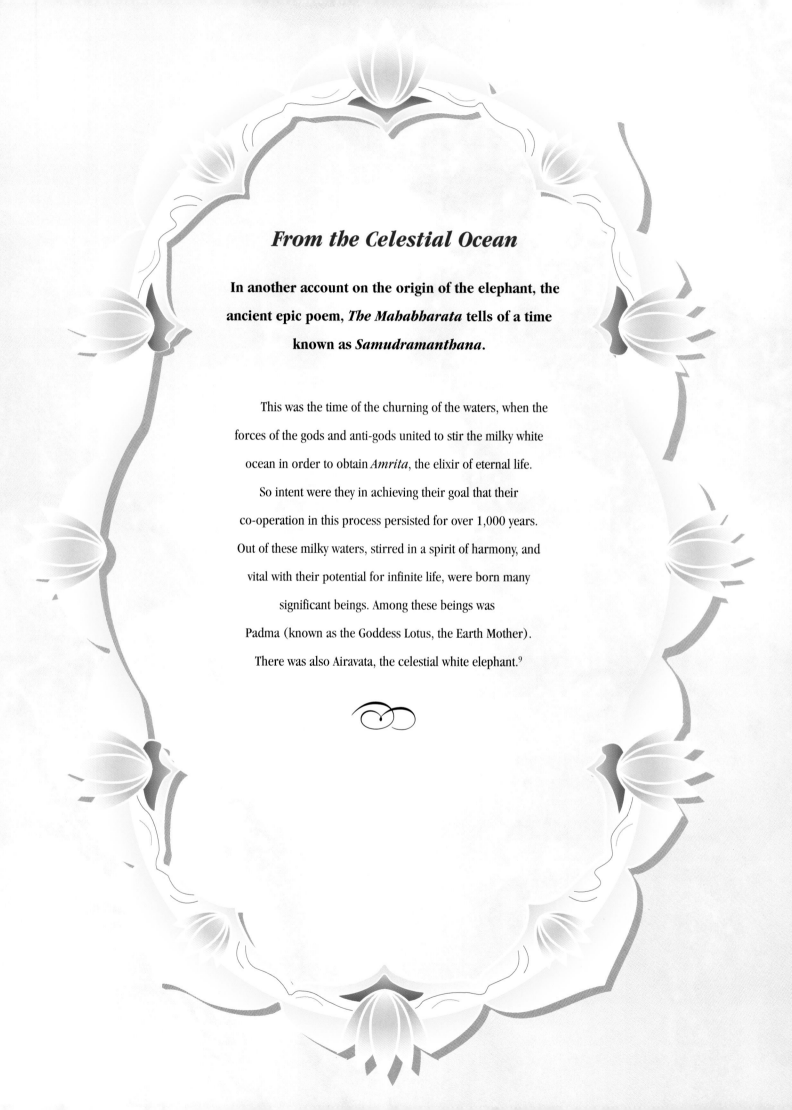

From the Celestial Ocean

In another account on the origin of the elephant, the ancient epic poem, *The Mahabharata* tells of a time known as *Samudramanthana*.

This was the time of the churning of the waters, when the forces of the gods and anti-gods united to stir the milky white ocean in order to obtain *Amrita*, the elixir of eternal life. So intent were they in achieving their goal that their co-operation in this process persisted for over 1,000 years. Out of these milky waters, stirred in a spirit of harmony, and vital with their potential for infinite life, were born many significant beings. Among these beings was Padma (known as the Goddess Lotus, the Earth Mother). There was also Airavata, the celestial white elephant.[9]

FROM MYTHS TO BELIEFS

Jewels of the Heavens

From the time when people and nature were more closely aligned, animals were considered sacred. The elephant's emergence from the celestial ocean bestows upon it characteristics of the divine, of the hallowed. Elephants have often been referred to as the *celestial ratnas*, or jewels of the heavens. As Zimmer, the noted expert on myths and symbols says, they are *the symbolic mounts of kings.*[10] For thousands of years they have served as the actual mounts of representations of gods or of relics (remains) of the Buddha. Today in Sri Lanka the traditions continue. In the ceremonies elephants carry ornate caskets containing such sacred items.

They are the symbolic mounts of kings.

Protection, Strength and Support

As the *dig-gajas*, or pillars of the universe, elephants uphold the cosmos, the whole of creation. They therefore symbolise strength and protection. Throughout Sri Lanka this symbol is reflected in the elephant walls around the many temples on the island. The ancient chronicle of Ceylon, *The Mahavamsa*, proudly describes the completion of the elephant wall, *Hatthipakara*, at the great Thupa (domed religious edifice enclosing a relic chamber) in the ancient capital of Anuradhapura, between 137 BC and 115 BC.

> *The wall...was built and the same was adorned with 400 elephant faces, which arrangement produced an impression of 400 elephants, 100 on each side of the dagaba, [relic chamber], watching it.*[11]

A remnant of one of 400 elephant carvings which formed a protective wall around the Thupa in the ancient city of Anuradhapura.

Givers and Sustainers of Life

In all cultures, water is vital. It is the source of life, rendering soils fertile for successful production. Abundant crops ensure a healthy and prosperous population. An animal associated with water is a special animal. Having emerged from the celestial ocean, elephants easily assume such association. This relationship is strengthened by their early ability to fly 'like clouds'.

Elephants are clouds sentenced to walk on the earth.[12]

Their relatives, the clouds, are lured to them. Therefore elephants attract rain. Possessing elephants or being in their presence ensures rain. A king who owned elephants guaranteed rain, fertility, crops and wellbeing for his people. So elephants have also been known as the *King's Clouds.*[13]

The association of the elephant with rain is apparent in the names of the first two elephants to be born of the Cosmic Egg, those which guide the eastern corner. Airavata means rainbow and lightning, whereas Abhramu is *she who produces clouds.* Airavata became the mount of the god Indra, who is the god of rain.

So essential is water that it became the focus for elaborate festivities where people prayed for rain or celebrated its arrival. Current day ceremonies in Sri Lanka can be traced to these notions. In these processions up to 100 elephants may participate.

The processions are an imitation of Indra [the god of rain] going about in procession in heaven...the elephants represent the rain clouds.[14]

The Elephant and the Lotus

The legend which describes the emergence of the white elephant, Airavata, from the cosmic ocean, the same source as the goddess Lotus, strengthens the link between elephants, fertility and prosperity. The goddess Lotus is the Earth Mother, the 'mother of the world'. She is the female principle through which creation takes form. She is always with the lotus; the flower whose monumental symbolism represents the 'womb of the universe', the ultimate truth, the ultimate wisdom of enlightenment.[15]

Later known as Sri Lakshmi, the goddess Lotus is consort to the god Vishnu, the protector of Buddhism in Sri Lanka. She is the goddess of abundance, wellbeing, prosperity and fertility. That the first elephant, the cosmic white elephant Airavata, the ancestor to all elephants should emerge from the same source as the goddess Lotus, links all elephants with the essential principles; the principles of fertility and creation, wisdom and abundance.

Two to 3,000 years ago, a North Indian festival regularly celebrated the cosmic female principle, aspects of fertility, rainfall, abundance and procreation. The white elephant, central to these festivities, was worshipped and honoured.

For indeed:

...if due worship is paid to the elephant,...[all] will thrive and prosper...Crops will sprout in due time; Indra, the rain god, will send rain in due time; there will be no plague; no drought. [Human life will span] a hundred years...The earth will abound in treasures of precious metals and jewels.[16]

The worshipping of the elephant on earth evokes a response in its heavenly kin.

[Such veneration] bestows all those earthly blessings which the goddess Lotus, Sri Lakshmi, Fortune and Prosperity, the Mother Earth, fertile and abundant with water and riches, has in store.[17]

The Elephant and the Moon

Sinhala astrology assigns an animal to each celestial body. To the moon is assigned the elephant, a fitting association since the moon is endowed with many aspects already associated with the elephant. The moon's residence is a watery place; its sex is female. Its nature, delicate; its colour white. It has royal rank. Its deity is the Water Deity. It is Lord of the Mind. Its metal is silver; its gem the pearl and its season is rainy.[18]

Elephants as Symbols

Elephants have become significant symbols throughout Sri Lanka. As well as the elephant walls already mentioned, elephant statues guard the entrance to many temples.

At the foot of many temple steps around Sri Lanka is the *Sandakada-pahana* (moonstone). This semi-circular stone symbolises the mastery over human desires to attain enlightenment. Desires are depicted as flames of fire and creepers, whereas Nirvana (enlightenment) is symbolised by the lotus flower in the centre. Four animals representing the stages of life are portrayed on the moonstone. The elephant is the symbol of birth, the bull represents decay, the lion disease and the horse, death. The repetition of these animals around the inner circumference of the moonstone suggests the cycle of life and reincarnation.

Paintings and sculptures of elephants adorn temple ceilings and walls in Sri Lanka. And often the inner sanctum is arched by huge elephant tusks. Such tusks may have been gifted to the temple in ceremonial offering, and their presence is considered to bring good fortune.

In Sri Lanka the sound of an elephant is considered opportune; the trumpeting is particularly auspicious. Even to dream of an elephant, especially a white one, will bring good luck and fortune. Elephants are said to bring a secure future. For this reason elephant bones have been placed within the foundations of buildings in the belief that this will augur well for the construction and those who use it.[19]

Rubbing the jaw bone of an elephant on the face of a child suffering with mumps is said to give immediate relief and a speedy recovery.[20] For some, the elephant placenta is particularly valued. It is dried and crushed to a powdered form. Small amounts are given with liquid to women undergoing difficult labour. Those familiar with this treatment describe how it instantly reduces the pain, releases the baby and results in a successful birth.

Having been born of the celestial and divine realms, the elephant has woven its way into mythology and become a profound symbol of strength, protection and fortune. For those who have been touched by the myths, the elephant is not only a symbol which inspires and reassures; it is also a sacred creature providing life and sustenance and therefore deserving of deep gratitude, honour and reverence.

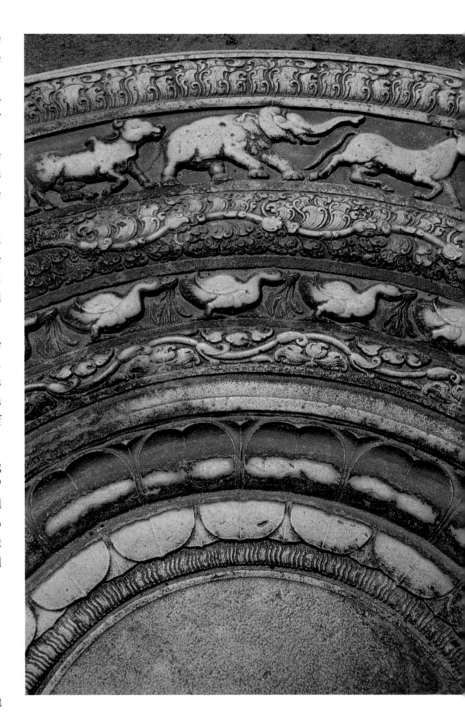

The elephant on the moonstone symbolises birth. The repetition of animal symbols around the inner circumference of the moonstone suggests the cycle of life, death and reincarnation.

ELEPHANTS AND BUDDHISM

E LEPHANTS have always been significant in Buddhist practice and ritual. Indeed, the Buddha was an elephant in some of his previous incarnations. He was conceived of an elephant, and when alone during his long fast he was attended and cared for by an elephant. In his teachings he often used the elephant as a metaphor.

Not only is Buddhism the predominant belief system in Sri Lanka, but for many, Sri Lanka is the protector of the Buddhist faith – the Dhammadipa, island of the Buddhist Teaching. The esteem ascribed to the elephant in Sri Lanka can be attributed in part to its significance within the Buddhist belief system.

The Birth of the Buddha

One summer, some 2,500 years ago, in the region of Kapilvastu, nestled in the foothills of the Himalaya, Queen Maya was celebrating the summer moon festival.

Rising early on the seventh day of the festival, she bathed in scented water and gave 400,000 pieces as alms. Fully adorned she ate the choicest food, took the upostha vows and lay down on the bed in her elaborate bed chamber. There she fell asleep. She dreamed of four kings, who raised her together with her bed, and taking her to the Himalaya set her beneath a great sala tree, seven leagues high. They stood on one side. Then the four queens came and took her to the Anotta Lake, bathed her to remove her human stains, robed her in heavenly clothing, anointed her with perfumes and bedecked her with divine flowers. Not far away was a silver mountain on which was a golden mansion. There they prepared a divine bed with its head to the east, and laid her upon it. Not far from there, there was a golden mountain. The Bodhisattva, in the form of a white elephant, descended from it and alighted on the silver mountain. He approached it from the direction of the north. In his trunk, which was like a silver rope, he held a white lotus. He entered the golden mansion, made a rightwise circle three times around Queen Maya's bed, smote her right side, and appeared to enter her womb.

The next day the queen told her dream to her husband, King Suddhodhana. He summoned 64 eminent Brahmans, gave them their due honour and satisfied them with excellent food and other presents.

Then he asked them to explain the significance of the dream. The Brahmans said, 'Be not anxious, O King. The queen has conceived and thou shalt have a son. If he dwells in the house he shall become a king, a universal monarch; if he leaves his house, and goes forth into the world he will become a Buddha, a remover in the world of the veil (of ignorance).' [21]

The queen's womb took the appearance of a crystal casket. She retired to the forest to meditate and there under the sal tree she gave birth to a boy looking like the sun. At the place where he touched the earth a lotus grew. He looked to the positions of the celestial elephants, the four cardinal points and the points in between. There, deities were honouring him. [22]

Varying stories exist as to the paternity of the Buddha. Some claim Queen Maya eager for a child, prayed to the elephant headed god, Ganesha, and that her request was granted. Others state that Ganesha came to the queen in an apparition. At that very moment she conceived. Whatever the story, it is generally believed that the birth of the Buddha is connected to an elephant. Thus the association between the Buddha and the elephant was established. In this sense the elephant assumes the role similar to that of the dove at the conception of Christ.[23]

Elephants as Representations of the Buddha

Just as elephants were considered *celestial ratnas* or divine jewels, so too the Buddha was seen as a rare and special divine being. The Emperor Asoka, who sent his son Mahinda from India to Sri Lanka to introduce the Buddhist teachings, believed the elephant to be a strong symbol of Buddhism. Initially it was considered improper to create images of the Buddha, so plants and animals were used as representations. In this way the elephant was used to characterise the Buddha.

Top: The inner sanctum of a temple is often arched by huge elephant tusks, as their presence is said to bring good fortune. Such tusks may have been presented in ceremonial offering.

Above: Elephants are significant in Buddhism. Here, in the ancient city of Anuradhapura, they are seen with the teaching Buddha.

The Buddha
and the Elephant Gift

The Jataka (Stories of the Buddha's former lives) illustrates
many incidents of the association of the Buddha with elephants.

In a previous incarnation, the Buddha came to earth as the King Vessantara. As a
king he was responsible for the welfare of his people, ensuring that they had
sufficient food, water and other essential amenities. One way of ensuring
adequate water for abundant crops was to possess elephants – the clouds, the
bringers of rain. As a king he owned many elephants. Amongst his elephants
was a white one, and therefore a particularly auspicious one.

In the neighbouring kingdom there was a severe drought. People were starving and
in their desperation many turned to crime. The people demanded of their king that he
obtain King Vessantara's *beautiful elephant all white...wherever he goes the rain falls...*

King Vessantara was practising *Dana Paramita* (the virtue of donating). He gladly gave his
white elephant to ensure abundant rains in the neighbouring region. However his own people
were not so happy about his generosity. They had lost their white elephant,
the bringer of rain and good fortune. They feared the possible consequences – drought
and its accompanying suffering.

When the great elephant was given, trembled the town for fear.

In an act of rebellion the people banished their king.[24]

So important was the elephant to the people that they ousted their king when he gave it away.
However, the white elephant was particularly auspicious, as it signifies the
source of all elephants, that is the milky ocean of the heavens.

Throughout the history of Sri Lanka, elephants have been gifted. Even in this century the practice has
continued. In 1937, a baby elephant was captured in the wild and later was given to the Kandy Temple. That
elephant, Raja, became famous and is still revered for having carried the Buddha's relics in ceremonies
for almost half a century. More recently, Sri Lanka has gifted elephants to other countries including the
United States of America, Pakistan, Switzerland and Wales.

The Buddha, the Elephants
and Justice

In one of his previous births the Buddha was Prince Magha. As the men of his
village came to know him, they adopted his principles of charity and service for
others. In spite of their innocence, they were charged with robbery. The sentence
from the king was death by the trampling of elephants. However, as each elephant
was brought to the men it *trumpeted loudly* and walked away. Not one elephant
would harm the men. The king accused the men of placing a spell on
the elephants. They explained that their only spell was their
good deeds. Whilst they remained of good heart the
elephants would not harm them. The king was
impressed and rewarded them lavishly.[25]

The Calming of the Elephant Naligiri

Another story of the Buddha and an elephant involves Buddha's
cousin and rival, Devadatta.

Devadatta, who harboured a keen jealously of the Buddha, intoxicated the
elephant Naligiri, aroused and stimulated him and then enticed him to attack and
crush the Buddha. As the elephant approached the Buddha in a crazed and
demented state, people fled in fear. The Buddha however remained serene.
The elephant vacillated, then collapsed. Slowly he regained
his demeanour, and calmly approaching the Buddha he laid his head
on the ground before him and prostrated.[26]

It is a strongly held belief that the compassion and peace of the
Buddha subdued the raging elephant.

The Elephant and Compassion

In another of his incarnations, the Buddha was Chaddanta, a beautiful white elephant with six huge tusks,
who sacrificed his life. This self sacrifice by an elephant is closely aligned to the Buddhist philosophy of
compassion and service for others.[27]

Compassion and service of the elephant is further illustrated in the story of the Buddha's retreat.

One year during Vas (the Rains Retreat) the Buddha was unhappy with fighting and dissension in the Sangha
(community of monks). He therefore left and went to the forest to undertake his retreat in solitude. He spent
the entire retreat alone except for the company of the large elephant, Paraliya, which daily attended to his
needs. By rolling a rock that had absorbed the heat of the sun, into a pool of water, the elephant warmed
the pool for the Buddha to take a bath. Each day he collected fruits. Each morning he would present
the Buddha with soft twigs so he could clean his teeth.

*Like one long experienced in performing services for a Buddha, he would place the robe
and bowl in their correct place, provide water for washing the feet and fan him with
the branch of a tree to cool him and dispel his fatigue.*

After some time the monks came to the Buddha and persuaded him to return,
claiming that they had overcome their differences. He agreed to go with them.

The elephant was extremely distressed and began to cry. The Buddha
explained to the elephant that the time had come for him to leave and the
elephant must remain in the forest. The elephant accepted his fate, but
overcome by grief he
lay down and died. Because of his good deeds he was reborn as the god
Parileyyaka enjoying abundant heavenly pleasures.[28]

Here again the kindness and self serving nature of the
elephant expresses compassion, a concept
cherished by Buddhists for all sentient beings.

From the Teachings of the Buddha

During his life the Buddha offered many teachings where he used the elephant as a metaphor to emphasise his words. [29]

On Friendship

The elephant, Parileyyaka, looked after me all this time. He was indeed my very good friend, a true friend. If one has such a friend one should stick to him. But if one cannot find a good friend it is better to stay alone.

Likening Himself to an Elephant

Just as a great, well disciplined elephant...on a battlefield withstands the arrows released from a bow...so shall I endure [abuse].

On Overcoming Moral Difficulties

Just as the elephant, sunk in the mire, pulled himself from the bog and stood on firm ground...so you raise yourselves from the mud of moral defilements and put yourselves on the firm land of Nibbana.

On Living One's Life

Let one live alone and do no wrongs, care-free, like an elephant in the forest.

On the Simile of the Elephant's Footprint

The very first Buddhist teaching given in Sri Lanka was enunciated by the eminent monk Mahinda, in 306 BC when he introduced Buddhism to the island. Yet again the elephant was prominent. High on the Mihintale mountain, among the mango trees, the Venerable Mahinda delivered his first sermon based on the *Culahattipadupamasuttanta* (the *Lesser Discourse on the Simile of the Elephant's Footprint*).[30] The teaching speaks of the life of a monk and his attainments; the steps or footprints of truth.

The footprint of the elephant assumes an importance in Buddhist doctrine. Because the elephant is the largest animal, wherever it goes, so can anything else. It opens the way for all others. So too do the teachings of the Buddha.

That is why the doctrine of the Buddha is compared to the footprint of the elephant. The all comprehending wisdom of the enlightened one, in its circumference, encompasses and transcends all partial, limited forms of knowledge.[31]

The Future Buddha

For some the Buddha will come again. And in his next coming he will descend with majesty and solemnity as a fine young white elephant, with red head and gleaming tusks, lavishly adorned in gold and jewels.[32]

SINHALESE HISTORY
AND THE ELEPHANT

THE Sinhalese people comprise more than 70 per cent of the population of Sri Lanka. They arrived on the island 2,500 years ago from Northern India. The ancient Chronicle, *The Mahavamsa*, which profiles their heritage, depicts many occasions where elephants made a significant contribution to the history of Sri Lanka.

Arrival of the Relics

The year 306 BC, some 200 years after the Sinhalese arrived on Lanka, marked a significant transformation for many people on the island. In that year the Indian King Asoka, ardent in his desire to see the Buddhist message spread extensively, sent his son, the monk Mahinda, and his daughter, the nun Sanghamitta, to bring the teachings of the Buddha to Lanka. Thousands converted. Both these messengers of Buddhism would later be honoured with the titles Thera and Theri respectively, indicating their revered standing in Buddhist orders. The Thera Mahinda beseeched the king of Lanka, King Devanampiyatissa, to obtain relics of the Buddha, that is, vestiges of the Buddha and his former possessions. During his lifetime the Buddha had promised joy and blessings to those who came within the presence of his remains. Such relics would provide an impetus, a focus of inspiration for devotees. According to the Buddha's wishes, they would be housed in a *dagaba* (relic chamber) situated in a Thupa, a large domed or bell shaped structure.[33] The king agreed to obtain the relics, whereupon he was advised to practice fasting and abstinence. Having done so he adorned the city. Riding the state elephant in full ceremonial regalia, he went to receive the relics – a collar-bone and alms bowl of the Buddha.

The Thera Mahinda placed the relics on the Mihintale mountain in central Sri Lanka and the location of the first Buddhist teaching on the island. The elephant immediately dropped to his knees. The king understood this as one of the signs indicating that these were indeed the relics. Ecstatic, he placed the relics on the back of the elephant who *trumpeted joyfully* and paraded around the city, followed by monks and people.

Finally the elephant came to the area where the Thupa (domed structure) was to be built. He stood facing the east. The area was cleared and decorated, befitting the reception of such sacred items. But as the king attempted to remove the relics from the elephant's back the elephant resisted. The king, perplexed by the elephant's behaviour, asked for the Thera's advice. The Thera Mahinda replied:

He would fain have [them] put in a place that is equal to his back; therefore will he not suffer them to be taken down. [34]

So a mound was built the height of the elephant. Only when this was completed, garlanded and decorated, did the elephant permit the relics to be removed from his back. From that moment the elephant was appointed by the king to be guardian of the relics. He undertook his duties assiduously, continually circling the mound, until the Thupa was completed.

Prayer flags adorn the sacred bo-tree in the ancient capital of Anuradhapura. The tree, said to be more than 2,000 years old, is grown from a sapling of the tree under which Buddha gained enlightenment.

This modern shrine in Kataragama honours King Dutugemunu (who reigned from 161–137 BC) and his elephant, Kandula. Because of his courage in battle, Kandula was awarded by his king the 'Lordship over the whole of Lanka'.

The King's Elephant Selects the Sacred Site for the Thupa

The king's elephant used to roam wherever he liked, but he had a favourite spot, the *Kadamba-flower-thicket*. He liked to eat and cool down there. When it was noticed that the elephant favoured this place a *Hatthalhaka* (elephant post) was erected. One day the elephant did not eat and he refused food given to him. The king was disturbed by this and called the Thera Mahinda to explain why the elephant was behaving in this manner. The Thera replied:

The elephant would fain have a Thupa built in the Kadamba-flower-thicket. [35]

The king wasted no time in arranging for the sacred structure to be erected. In keeping with custom, a relic was enclosed.

The Theri Sanghamitta, since her arrival in Lanka, had established an order of nuns. She was greatly esteemed because she had brought to Sri Lanka a branch of the bo-tree, the very tree under which the Buddha had attained enlightenment. During his lifetime the Buddha had ordained that to honour the bo-tree was tantamount to honouring him. The bo-tree was planted in the ancient capital Anuradhapura, and is still there today. It is believed to be the oldest documented tree in the world.

Theri Sanghamitta was also skilful in identifying sacred places. She required a special place of seclusion to establish a convent for her nuns. She went to the site chosen by the elephant, the *Hatthalhaka* (elephant post). There she meditated. When the king heard of this, he granted her wish and built a convent on the site near the Thupa. It was called the *Hatthalhaka-vihara* (the elephant-post convent).

Kandula, a King's Elephant

Early in the second century BC a prince was born, with *all the auspicious attributes*. He was called Prince Gamani. At the time of his birth an elephant of the *Chaddanta* caste, of sacred and noble breed, arrived at the palace. The elephant's arrival and its high caste, were considered indicators of the prince's significance. The elephant was called Kandula. Both prince and elephant grew up together.

In adult years Prince Gamani opposed his father's wishes to live in peace with the neighbouring monarchs, and was subsequently known as Dutugemunu (the stubborn Gamani[36]). After his father's death Dutugemunu fulfilled his desire to *bring glory to the [Buddhist] doctrine*. To achieve this he wished to rid the land of Tamils and therefore declared war on Tamil princes. Many battles ensued. It is recorded that the elephant Kandula displayed fierce courage as he attacked city gates and walls in his efforts to undertake his master's bidding. At the area of Vijitanagara, Kandula was badly injured. With his back burning from molten lead he sought relief in the cool waters of a pond. He was treated for his wounds and encouraged by his King Dutugemunu:

To thee, I give dear Kandula, the lordship over the whole of the island of Lanka. [37]

With such encouragement, Kandula attacked the gate of the town crashing it to the ground. Wrenching a cart wheel on to his trunk he used it to assist King Dutugemunu's warriors take the town. The king continued to be successful in battle. However, his goal was to overthrow Elara, the Tamil King of the royal capital, Anuradhapura. Drawing near to the city he made the pronouncement:

None but myself shall slay Elara [38]

The two kings confronted each other on their respective elephants; King Elara on Mahapabbata, King Dutugemunu on Kandula. Fiercely they fought each other. As Kandula impaled Mahapabbata through the side with his tusk, King Dutugemunu cast his spear into King Elara. Both king and elephant fell to the ground and died. King Dutugemunu and his elephant Kandula paraded triumphantly, Dutugemunu claiming himself as the king of all of Lanka.

On hearing of the attack against King Elara, 60,000 of his supporters came to Anuradhapura to do battle. Mounted on Kandula, King Dutugemunu went forward to meet them just outside Anuradhapura. However, Kandula, after undertaking battle for some time, began to retreat. The king was stunned. Never before, in any battle, 28 to be exact, had his state elephant withdrawn from the scene until victory was theirs. In his confusion, the king asked his expert archer, Phussadeva, for an explanation. Phussadeva advised:

Victory lies behind...At the place of victory, [Kandula] will halt. [39]

The elephant finally came to stand beside the shrine of the deity, the guardian of the city close to the monastery. And there some time later, the battle was won by King Dutugemunu and his forces.

The achievements of Kandula are still remembered and revered today. In the holy city of Kataragama a special shrine has been erected in his honour. He is remembered because of his noble breed, his courage, skill and his strategic sense. But he is remembered particularly because he was very much responsible for uniting the land of Lanka under one rule. This, as his king proclaimed:

...[brought] glory to the doctrine [of the Buddha]. [40]

That an elephant would play such a significant role in establishing Buddhism in Sri Lanka is not forgotten. Devotees today proudly and happily relate the story in varying ways.

The Building of the Great Thupa

In approximately 120 BC, on the feast of Wesak, the celebration of the Buddha's birth and enlightenment, the King Dutugemunu arranged for work to start on the erection of the Great Thupa, the Ruwanweli *Dagaba* (relic chamber) in Anuradhapura.

To ensure that the earth was firm on which to hold such a mighty structure, elephants fitted with leather boots were used to trample and flatten the ground. Within the relic chamber the king placed the most sacred of objects; golden statues of the Buddha and a bo-tree made of gold and silver with the *eight auspicious figures*, one of whom is an elephant. Among other auspicious animals, elephant images were painted on the ceiling to protect the chamber from evil spirits. Frescoes depicting the Buddha's life were incorporated, including the story of how the Buddha calmed an aggressive elephant, Naligiri. When the relic chamber was complete the most elaborate of processions took place to celebrate the enshrining of the Buddha's relics. A golden casket containing the relics was placed on the back of Kandula, who was magnificent in his beautiful apparel. On arrival at the chamber the relics were enshrined.

The State Elephant Saves the King

In 37 AD the King Ilanaga ascended the throne. Soon after, he was captured and imprisoned by a clan of Lankans who were displeased with his orders. The queen, fearing for her little son, sent him with her lady in waiting to the state elephant with the order that the elephant kill the little boy.

Better it is for this [boy] to meet his death by thee than by the enemies. [41]

On hearing these words the state elephant ...*for grief...began to shed tears....*[42] Wrenching himself from his tethering post, he made his way quickly to the king in his prison. He crashed the gate, 'ordered' the king on to his back and carried him to Mahatittha. There he placed him on a ship, which took him to the west coast. The elephant retreated to the area called Malaya, the mountainous area of Sri Lanka.

Years later the king returned with an army to confront his detractors.

Then came the king's state elephant forthwith out of the southern Malaya to Rohana [now the area of Yala National Park] to do him [the king] service.[43]

The king was victorious in battle and regained the throne. In gratitude he allocated to his elephant the region of Malaya, where he had stayed during the king's absence. This land came to be known as *Hatthibhoga*, that is the 'fiefdom of the elephant'.[44]

This story affirms yet again how elephants in Sri Lanka have been honoured for their significant role. They have identified relics, selected sacred sites, brought about victory in battle and served as guardians and protectors. What other creature has had an entire nation dedicated to it?

SAMAN AND HIS LITTLE WHITE ELEPHANT

O Sri Sumana Saman
Whose look falls on the wilderness of the Samanala peak
The heavenly abode of the golden red coconut trees...
And on the elephant tusker vehicle
Who with goodness, looks with kindness on Sri Lanka...
Listen and accept merit from us
And because of this merit, protect us...[45]

IN the south east of the island of Sri Lanka, the almost perfect pyramidal shape of Adam's Peak **rises above the long undulating mountain range. At times within the clarity of the sky and lightness of the air it appears benign, a small peak, perched atop its mountainous base. At other times, shrouded in mist and swirling clouds, it becomes mysterious, incomprehensible.**

As if to match its varying ambiences, this peak has many names. Sri Pada commemorates the sacred footprint at the summit. To Buddhists, this is the imprint of the Buddha. For Muslims it marks Adam's visit to the island. Hence the name Adam's Peak. For Hindus, it is Shiva's footprint and for Christians it is that of St Thomas. But for many Sri Lankans, it is Sumanakuta, in honour of Saman, the guardian deity of the mountain and its region. Saman, with his little white elephant, is believed to be a good god, a god who heals the sick and brings rain for abundant agriculture. He has a special claim in the protection of Buddhism in Sri Lanka. But who is Saman really, what are his origins and what of his little white elephant? No-one quite knows.

For thousands of years, elephants roamed this mountain range, its gentle curves and valleys. Maybe in the ways of the elephant they surveyed the 360 degree view from the summit, meditating as they maintained their rhythmic stance. The cooler air would have resulted in less frequent ear flapping rendering them even more silent than usual. No doubt they would have witnessed many a sunrise and perhaps paid homage to the unique blue shadow of the pyramid projected into the heavens by the rising sun.

These elephants, the elephants of Sri Pada, were slightly smaller than the average Sri Lankan elephant. Even so, they were reputedly the strongest and most tenacious – characteristics acquired in their grapple with the precipitous terrain. They would have been witness to the many pilgrims who made their way to the summit in devotion to their respective gods.

They would have heard their chants 'Sadhu, Sadhu', Blessed, Blessed, to Saman for a safe journey, for a healing or for some other desired outcome. Maybe the pilgrims followed one of the many elephant pathways to the summit. These pathways, so obvious to the British engineer and road builder, Skinner, when he mapped the island in 1833, greatly assisted him in his work.

Today the elephants and elephant paths of Sri Pada have been replaced by tea plantations and their colourful pickers. Trinket peddlers surround the base of the mountain luring pilgrims into sales of baubles. And whilst the chants to Saman survive and linger, they do so amidst the raucous broadcasting of popular rock music from the numerous tea houses lining the pilgrim route to the summit.

Yet somehow the mountain remains beneficent and generous, surmounting the current trends as if more conscious of its past than the drift of its present. The elephants in their absence have yet a stronger presence.

For many the elephants have not gone. There is the little white elephant – Saman's little white elephant. Not little because he is of the local species but because of his tender age. Still today, for many he resides in *Diva Guhava*, the cave at the bottom of the mountain. It was to this special place that Saman brought the Buddha after he had imprinted his foot at the summit. In the little white elephant's trunk is a pink lotus, symbolising the lotus he presented Saman on his first visit to the Buddha's footprint. This enabled Saman to make the flower *puja* (offering). The white elephant represents sovereignty and divinity. Therefore, to be in his presence, Saman is himself attributed with these characteristics.[46]

Some believe, that twice a year, at *Navam Poya* (February full moon) and *Wesak Poya* (the Buddha's birthday), the little white elephant leaves his cave and goes all the way to the top of the mountain to honour the deity Saman.

Opposite: At sunrise on a clear day, the shadow of Sri Pada (Adam's Peak) is projected into the heavens. This mountain, sacred to Buddhists, Hindus, Muslims and Christians is also the dwelling place of the deity Saman who is accompanied by his little white elephant.

THE ELEPHANT HEADED GOD
GANESHA

WHO is this deity with an elephant head and human form? His ears are wide, his trunk large. His round pot belly perches on his crossed legs. His feet are fat and squat. He usually hides his ankles. Why is he accompanied by a little mouse, or a rat which he mounts, or even a cow?

What is it about this deity, who appears distorted yet enticing, asymmetrical yet poised, alien yet known?

They call him Lord Ganesha and throughout Sri Lanka decorative *kovils* (shrines) and temples stand dedicated to him. Although predominantly Hindu, his carved form appears in some Buddhist temples.

So who is this deity Ganesha? And what does he mean? Opinions differ...

'This is Lord Ganesha. And these are his wives' said the young boy displaying his pictures at a small stall along the pilgrim path. But the old woman inside the Ganesha temple could barely contain her wrath. 'Wives! Lord Ganesha – he has no wives. Lord Ganesha is a bachelor. He is a singular deity and as such he helps people follow a spiritual path that is uncontaminated by distractions'.

From well wishers...

'Worship Lord Ganesha and your book will be a great success. He is the Lord of Obstacles. He will remove obstacles from your path. And he will place obstacles in your path, if you need them. Then again he will place obstacles in the path of those who may wish to thwart you. He is the Lord of Beginnings. Before you start your work you must entreat him. He is the Lord of Writing'. And there was often a final caution, 'But you must believe'.

'It is true' said the woman who professed to be a Christian. 'I always go to him. He will make things happen'.

Yet another well wisher advised us: 'Your book is about elephants, no? Then we must go to the priest. He will perform the ritual to the Lord Ganesha. That way you will have every success. I am Muslim but I believe'.

From the Buddhist monk and scholar...

'He is simply a decoration to appease the Indian wives of the kings'.

For those participating with their elephants in the ceremonies...

'Ganesha is the Chief of the elephants'. They visit his shrine and seek his blessings.

At the Ganesha Temple...

The man clasped his hands, bowed and exclaimed, 'Oh my God, the Lord Ganesha. I come to his temple for refuge. In this country of such atrocities, the truth is no more. Here I can find truth. Here I can be at peace'.

And after the *Puja* (Offering)...

'Eat this food. It is blessed, in the Ganesha Temple. It is sacred food.
When you eat this you must be successful'.

Opposite: The Sri Selva Vinayagar Temple in Kandy abounds with lush images of the elephant headed deity, Ganesha.

GANESHA'S MANY NAMES

Some say Ganesha has a thousand names, each depicting a divine quality which he embodies.

Ganesha

Ganapati

    Lord of Hosts

    Lord of Categories

Vakratunda

    He of the Curved Trunk

Ekadanta

    He of the Single Tusk

Omkaraswarupa

    Personification of OM

Vinayaka

    Lord of Obstacles (This name is also interpreted as Lord of the Holy Breath of Life)

Kanapathy

    Lord of Sound

And the Litany continues:

    Lord of Lords

    Lord of the World

    Radiating Lustre

    Knowledge and Bliss

    Path to Success

    Inexhaustible One

    Pure One

    Ingenious One

    Manifestation of the Unmanifest

    He of Good Face

    He Whose Actions are Rhythmical

    He Who is Love

    He Whose Form is Existence

As the god of a thousand names, the whimsical elephant faced, Lord Ganesha is aptly titled. He represents a myriad concepts to his devotees. But who is he and why is he so popular? Unravelling the mystery that is Ganesha is impossible, but at the same time challenging and fruitful. The process is a journey into an intriguing world of infinite possibilities.

Ganesha emanates from a mythological web, woven with legendary tales from the simple parable to a complex esoteric. He is born and re-born sometimes of woman only, sometimes of man only, sometimes of woman and man. He is born human attaining his elephant upper form in later years. Sometimes he is born elephant. He stands, he sits, he dances. His trunk may turn right, it may turn left. He is sexual; he is asexual. He has two, four, six, eight hands. He is always pot bellied, always humorous, always beneficent. In his myriad stances, representations and symbolisms, Ganesha guides his devotees along a path that may be conventional and rudimentary or penetrating and profound. And all the time, the path is laced with humour. After all, the path to enlightenment can be fun.

At one time, in the time of the matriarchs, Ganesha was born of the goddess Parvati. She fashioned him from the dust of her body, and blessed him with water. At another time he was born of both Parvati and Shiva, who responding to the pleas from the chief god Indra, created Ganesha to intervene in the wars of the gods and anti-gods. By prudently positioning or removing obstacles, Ganesha restored peace to the celestial realms. Through this restoration he embodies a sense of harmony and justice. And yet another time, Parvati and Shiva were ambling through the forest when they saw two elephants making love. They marvelled at the beauty and tenderness of their actions. Both Parvati and Shiva transformed themselves into elephants and created Ganesha.

However born, of woman or man, as human or elephant, Ganesha was always the eldest son of the goddess Parvati and the god Shiva. As with his many births, he acquired his elephant features in numerous ways.

Ganesha was his mother's protector. And in this role, whilst desperately guarding her privacy, he fought his father, who severed his head. Parvati enraged at her son's demise ordered Shiva to the forest to obtain the head of the first animal he saw. He returned with an elephant's head which bonded perfectly to the son. Parvati was pleased. Shiva named him *Lord of the Ganas*, the heavenly hosts and determined that he be the first to be worshipped at any ritual. So Ganesha became the Lord of Beginnings.

With his demise and subsequent rebirth, Ganesha embodies the concept of life and death originating from the same source. Yet again this moment of transition is seen as progression from the human to the divine. So Ganesha is the reminder, the symbol of this potential.

In one of Shiva's creations of Ganesha, he was a beautiful young man. Parvati, concerned that his beauty may distract the heavenly beings, ordered that he bear the head of an elephant.

In each aspect of his being Ganesha reminds his devotees of a path beyond the material, beyond the ordinary. With outstretched ears he discriminates sounds capturing only those of truth and wisdom. The untruths float away on the breeze created by his flapping ears. But his association with sound is even more meaningful. His profile resembles the Sanskrit letters for the word OM, the sacred sound. He is the manifestation of the resonant OM.

His trunk denotes wisdom. Yet again it signifies the breath of life, that flow which connects internal and external. When curved, his trunk portrays a circuitous path to wisdom. To the right it speaks of a conventional and blessed path, whereas to the left it is unorthodox.

With his complete tusk Ganesha intimates the figure '**1**', the beginning. This is also the mark of unity, of singular nature, of strength and power. His other tusk, the broken one, symbolises the discarding of the ego, so essential to acquiring wisdom, which he embodies in diverse ways. Having torn it from his body, Ganesha used it to write the *Mahabharata*, as dictated by the sage Vyasa. The fluidity and clarity of this Indian epic are attributed to the two conditions set by Ganesha; that the sage dictate continuously, without pauses or vacillations and that the entire dictation be understandable to Ganesha. With this he became renowned as the Patron of Writers, the God of Wisdom and Learning.

He gave up his tusk in many ways and at many times. In surrendering it for service to others he expresses compassion. The wise are compassionate.

Beneath his head and trunk, his pot belly expands expressing space, the infinite. Filled with *modaka* (sweets and fruits), his swollen belly is abundant and fertile with the seeds of life.

With two hands he is human. With more than two hands he is more than human. With his hands Ganesha bestows blessings, gives refuge and protection.

The elephant, the largest animal, can go anywhere. It can remove any obstacle in its path. Once an elephant has been, so too can anyone. So Ganesha, the elephant headed god, is aptly the Lord of Obstacles. Combined with his vehicle the rat, he is all powerful. The rat too can go anywhere. The rat survives all.

The rat is also the symbol of darkness. Ganesha brings light. As such Ganesha overcomes darkness. From ignorance he enlightens.

With bell in hand, Ganesha represents protection; with the ankus or goad, discernment and discrimination. The noose is a reminder of the perils of bonding to wordly things. It invokes freedom from bondage – the detachment essential to understanding beyond the material. [47]

Ganesha has been bachelor, spouse, even parent. He is male and female, Ganeshini. To some, his wives, *Buddhi* (Wisdom) and *Siddhi* (Success), are the expression of his own attributes.

As elephant god, Ganesha enables his devotees to experience all the divine attributes of the elephant. As the elephant headed one, with human form and divine qualities, he represents the oneness of nature, human and the divine.

For the young pubescent boy, selling his gaudy pictures, of course Ganesha has wives. For the old lady he is a singular deity. For the man pained and tortured by the atrocities of war, Ganesha is peace and refuge. And for almost all his devotees he is the remover of obstacles. His humour allows him flexibility.

At the Buddhist temple in Kelaniya near Colombo, the elephant deity Ganesha perches on his vehicle, the rat.

Why he was born dazzlingly beautiful only to be disfigured, in most cases by his parents, is one of mythology's unsolved mysteries. It could be an atavistic clinging to animal worship; equally, a wholesome respect for and acceptance of the animal world and a desire to pay it the ultimate tribute of divinity. It might just possibly be an indulgence in the aesthetic of the absurd, a stroke of elephantine humour. We shall never know. [48]

Whoever he is and whatever he means, one thing remains true. In Ganesha, the form and aspects of the elephant are vehicles to an understanding of the deepest and most complex of concepts.

TWO

PHYSICAL
ATTRIBUTES

ELEPHANT CASTES

NCIENT Sanskrit and Pali texts talk of elephant castes, diseases and their cures, spirits that rule the various parts of the elephant's body, methods of capture and training and the use of the ankus – the goad for elephant discipline. Much of the information contained in the texts is contingent on the caste of the elephant. The caste system codifies elephants into good and bad, lucky and unlucky. At times the categorisation is complex, determined by factors including geographical location, height, weight, colour, dimensions and numerous other physical attributes. At times it is ambiguous. In Sri Lanka, such knowledge was considered important for the nobility and even today many believe this knowledge crucial to the health and wellbeing of the elephant.

Ancient Sinhala Elephant Lore is linked to mythology and divides elephants into ten distinct castes and numerous sub-categories. High caste elephants, such as the Chaddanta, have noble attributes of *golden hair covering the body and nails shaped like the waxing moon*.[49] They are said to bring honour and fame. Low caste elephants have bizarre and unpleasant characteristics. Watery eyes and moronic looks spell sadness; whereas conspicuous testicles[50] are indicative of a mean elephant. Low caste elephants are associated with death and destruction.

European settlers in Ceylon quickly became aware of the extent to which those who owned or worked with elephants were in possession of an extraordinary knowledge.

So conversant are the natives with the structure and points of the elephant, that they divide them readily into castes, and describe with particularity their distinctive excellences and defects.[51]

In ancient and colonial times such knowledge was highly revered. Today it is synthesised with contemporary elephant management.

There are some interesting instances of the merging of ancient knowledge and modern practices. One such example is the Veterinarian's Report (1988) on the death of Raja, the revered temple elephant.[52] That the foremost statement in this scientific report identifies the elephant's caste, indicates an ongoing respect for such ancient knowledge.

Those who continue to abide by the ancient practices and beliefs claim that to do so is to ensure happy and harmonious relations between elephants and people.

Elephant Castes

Name	Characteristics Attributed to Each Caste	Outcome for Owner
Kalavaka kule	Colour black, eyes round like a crow's and brownish in colour, head rounded and set awkwardly on body in an erect manner, ears soft, lips like a crow's beak and four inches thick from the middle of the teeth, limbs short, tail and nails curved. This elephant is regarded as strong but lazy. It is revengeful in nature.	Brings bad luck to its owner.
Gangeye kule	Black haired, head large, trunk broad at its base and elongate, ears are shovelled and with tufts of hair, limbs elongate with hands and feet broad, nails large and rounded, lips five inches thick, 100 years life span. Trumpeting fierce.	Brings misfortune to its owner.
Pandara kule	Body grey, nails yellow, eyes blue in colour, head long and broad, base of trunk thick, quick in movement. Life span 88 years. The odour resembles that of a jackal.	Will ruin the owner.
Thambe kule	Eyes, body and nails copper coloured, head of medium size, trunk weak and freckled, eyes round, ears narrow, limbs elongate and slender, lips six inches thick, quick in movements. Does not perspire, trumpeting very unpleasant.	Brings death to the king and heir.
Pingala kule	Whitish in colour, head large and spotted, base of trunk broad, eyes somewhat elongate and whitish, tail elongate with a very hairy tuft at its end, limbs moderate, hands and feet large.	Brings destruction upon the owner and clan.
Gandha kule	Colour of dark rain cloud, body and skin hard like stone, very hairy, head small, trunk small, nails pale black, tail elongate and kinked, easily enraged. Eyes resemble those of a drongo. Trumpeting powerful, likes company.	Confers good and bad luck on owner.
Mangala kule	Eyes rather dark, nails reddish, head and trunk large, eyes rounded, ears large, body stout, hands and feet large, tail elongated and touches the ground, its root large, disposition kindly.	Arrogant but harmless.
Hema kule	Colour whitish, head and trunk spotted, nails reddish, eyes light, body stout. A deep hollow exists on the top of the head, eyes like those of a mule. Fond of good food.	Brings good luck and bad luck.
Uposatha kule	Body light coloured, eyes red, nails golden. Trunk, penis and tail touch the ground. Toe nails resemble lotus petals. Gait resembles that of a parrot.	Brings wealth and longevity to the king.
Chaddanta kule	Body and eyes golden in colour, nails resemble light coloured sealing wax, eyes elongate, limbs of medium length, hands and feet elongate, not very hairy, trunk, penis and tail touch the ground. This elephant does not lose its temper, even when molested. It is fond of dainty food. Its life span is 120 years.	Brings fame and honour to the king.[53]

THE ANATOMY
OF THE ELEPHANT

SRI LANKAN NAMES
FOR THE ELEPHANT

SINHALESE

Aliya (Also generic term for elephant)	Tush elephant
Atha	Male with tusks
Ek-Danteya	Single tusk male
Athinne	Female with tushes
Pussa	Male with no tusks or tushes
Alidena	Female with no tushes
Kurundu Atha	Aliya with the bodily characteristics and trumpet note of the Atha[56]

TAMIL

Yanai	Generic term for elephant

OMETIMES elephants appear rock-like. Their black bulk, fresh out of water, glistens like granite. They stand firm and motionless, as though even time cannot erode their presence.

Other times, elephants are barely visible. Like wispy clouds they move and merge with the trees, with the grass and even with the sky, leaving in their wake a vague but memorable notion rather than a solid construction.

In which ever way elephants appear, their presence can be overwhelming yet strangely reassuring. Their contours evoke a landscape that is as rugged and mysterious as it is familiar and seductive.

These massive creatures, with their lithe gentle gait, often stand with one rear leg tucked daintily behind the other. With their domed head, flapping freckled ears, flowing trunk, straight or crinkled tail, they beg the question – what is an elephant?

A Unique Subspecies

The Sri Lankan elephant, *Elephas maximus maximus*, is a subspecies of the Asian elephant, *Elephas maximus*. As such it has many features in common with its mainland cousin. But it maintains a unique identity due to these characteristics:

† **Depigmentation:** Of all Asian elephants the Sri Lankan elephant appears to have more accentuated pale markings on the head, trunk and ears.[54]

† **Degree of Tusklessness:** Of Sri Lankan elephants, only ten per cent of the males bear tusks. This is a less frequent occurrence than in other Asian subspecies where tusks are evident in both sexes.

† **Size:** Sri Lankan elephants are usually larger and have more prominent foreheads than their mainland Asian cousins.[55]

African Elephants

Sri Lankan Elephants

Two species of elephants remain on the earth – the Asian, *Elephas maximus*, and the African, *Loxodonta africana*. The Sri Lankan elephant is a subspecies of the Asian elephant. While both the Asian and African elephants share many common features, there are some marked physical differences. The Asian elephant is usually of a smaller build and lighter colour than the African elephant. Its skin is smoother than that of the African elephant which is more wrinkled and less hairy. It also has smaller ears but a more prominent dome-shaped head and an arched back. The trunk of the Asian elephant has one finger tip, the African elephant has two. Both male and female African elephants have tusks, but only ten per cent of Sri Lankan male elephants have tusks. The Sri Lankan elephant is further differentiated by depigmentation on the head, trunk and ears.

Parts of the Elephant's Body

As Recognised by Mahouts – the Elephant Keepers

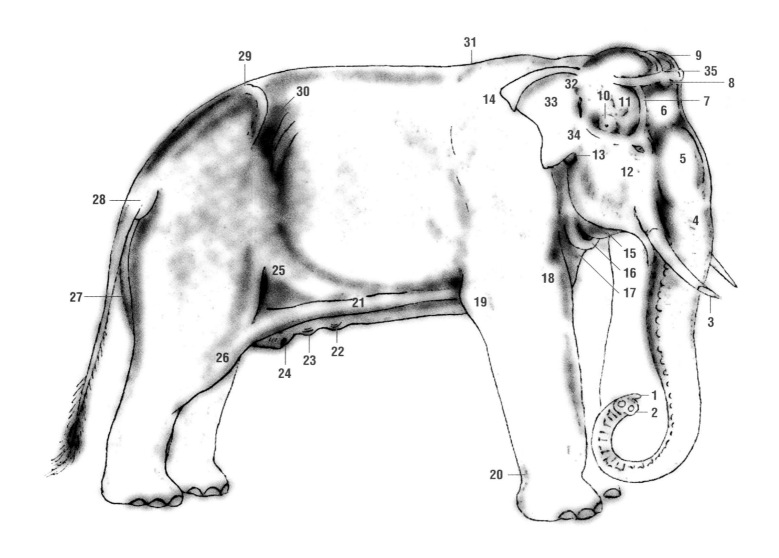

1 Sonda angilla – **finger**	13 Hiri labu pola – **post auricular prominence**	25 Nidipola – **flank**
2 Sonda nala – **trunk tip**	14 Kane ralla – **ear fold**	26 Pasa dhana – **knee**
3 Dhala madhima – **surface of wear on tusk**	15 Thalla – **dewlap**	27 Kosha thalla – **perenial fold**
4 Sonda mula – **base of trunk**	16 Male – **transverse throat fold**	28 Paha kumbe – **anal fold**
5 Pera Kumbe – Bopatha – **nasal bump**	17 Thalli vala – **brisket**	29 Pasa Asene – **sacral area** or **rear seat for mahout**
6 Nalala – **forehead**	18 Ura handiya – **biceps**	30 Ala vala, Halla vala – **flank**
7 Dhebami recava – **fronto-parietal ridge**	19 Vala mita handiya – **elbow**	31 Isaraha asene – **seat**
8 Otunu marla gate – **frontal ridge bump**	20 Vilangu pola – **wrist**	32 Uda savaka – **upper flap or pinna**
9 Kapolas thale – **vertex**	21 Akni thalle – **inguinal lateral fold**	33 Kane horuva – **ear opening**
10 Madha vala – **temporal gland**	22 Kunu pekaniya – **umbilicus**	34 Yata savaka – **lobe of pinna**
11 Muthu vala – **temple**	23 Hindi noola – **post umbilical prominence**	35 Otunu marlava – **frontal ridge**
12 Adhara pola – **cheek tuft**	24 Kosa pola – **opening of penis sheath**	Diagram based on Dr P.E.P Deraniyagala's work. [57]

Size

Large bones and broad chest...

Broad and long cheeks.

Large fat body.

[These characteristics] indicate longevity. [58]

Each new encounter with an elephant is a reminder, yet again, of the enormity of these wondrous creatures. In Sri Lanka, these shapely giants weigh between 3,000 to 5,000 kilos. With composure and dignity they realise a height of between two and a half and three and a half metres and a similar length when measured from eye to tail. Indeed the largest recorded Asian elephant was Sri Lankan. Shot in 1882, this elephant measured just over three and a half metres and weighed 7,257 kilos.[59]

A traditional method of determining the height of an elephant to the shoulder, is to measure the circumference of the forefoot and double it.

With her trunk the mother establishes
a powerful and potent bond.

Trunk

Elephants with a large trunk with the trunk finger always moving, will bring destruction upon the king's sons and ministers...

but

Elephants with a long and slender trunk may bring prosperity and happiness. [60]

Elephants with indentations along the under side of the trunk are exceptional and considered to bring good fortune.

When two elephants meet, it is the trunks that meet first. While together, they constantly stroke and touch. Their exploration is detailed and delicate. And when they make love, their trunks form the centrepiece of an extended foreplay akin to the symmetry of the petal of the lotus.

In Sanskrit, the elephant is *Mriga Hastin*, the animal with the hand, since it employs its trunk as a hand. This remarkable instrument, the merging of the nose and extended upper lip, is used to eat, drink, breathe and bathe. It is one of the most versatile limbs on any living creature.

[It can] delicately remove a tiny Mimosa inflorescence [collection of minute blossoms] or bring down a stout branch from a height of five metres.

For its sheer range this capability is unsurpassed by any other terrestrial herbivore. [61]

When the newborn infant lies vulnerable beneath its mother's huge mass, it is her vast trunk that is extended to delicately caress and reassure. Exploring every crevice, every facet of her little one, the mother registers its uniqueness, establishing a powerful and potent bond. Simultaneously her trunk will lift and guide the little one onto its own feet, positioning it beneath her belly so that it can reach her nipples and receive nourishment.

In the heat of the day, the elephant employs its trunk to scoop large quantities of water or dust, and raising the trunk above its head, showers the contents over its body, thus cooling and insulating itself.

When danger threatens, the trunk can act as an early warning device or an instrument for scaring foes. A loud trumpeting, broadcast through the trunk may be a signal, not just to immediate family, but also to distant colleagues. Air expelled through the trunk may create a mini dust storm, and serve to frighten and deter intruders.

The Trunk of the Sri Lankan Elephant:

† Has approximately 50,000 muscles and no bones

† Ends in one finger (Sonda angilla)

† Has two nostrils

† Weighs 125–200 kilos

† May be depigmented

† Can vary in length from one and a half to two metres

† Has a lifting capacity of 350 kilos and a cubic capacity of five to eight and a half litres

For protection an elephant may curl the trunk, placing the tip in its mouth. Guarding the trunk is crucial, since it is almost indispensable and once damaged the elephant may die.

Elephants use their trunks with delicacy, dexterity and deliberation. But however skilful, this does not come easy. A newborn elephant does not automatically know how to use its trunk. It frolics around, trunk dangling and wobbling in front, as if it is totally mystified by its purpose. Indeed a baby elephant appears clumsy and at the mercy of this long uncontrollable dangling proboscis. Its efforts to curl its trunk on the ground, assemble some food, lift this to its mouth, or strip bark are for the most part unsuccessful. When all else fails it may fall to its knees, by-pass its trunk and thrust its mouth into the food, in a desperate effort to eat. With practice and experience under the watchful supervision of its elders, it will eventually attain the same talent and adeptness that they display.

What Elephants do with their Trunks

† Touch and caress each other

† Breathe

† Drink

† Scoop up water, dust or mud:
  – to shower on themselves for coolness, or
  – to hurtle at some unwelcome entity

† Trumpet loudly

† Obtain food from places as low as the ground or as high as five metres

† Lift objects as small as a twig or as large as logs

† Use as a snorkel while swimming

† Rest them on their tusks, on other elephants or any nearby object

† Scratch themselves with a twig

† Grasp a small branch to swat flies

† Rub their eyes, their ears, their glands or any part of the body in need of a rub

† Lift calves when first born enabling them to stand and suckle

† Discipline calves with a sharp rap on the rump

† Insert into their colleague's anus

† Spar, particularly the males

† Fling rocks, wood or other objects at intruders

† Reach out, under and up a colleague's dress during the temple festivities

† Carry a gift from a monk, say a pineapple, all the way to a quiet spot where it can be eaten in solitude

† When newly born, make clumsy attempts to gain control

† Hold a friend's tail

If you're lucky enough to be near, an elephant may use its trunk to:

† Reach out and touch your hand

† Remove the contents of your pocket

† Inspect your bag

† Play tug-of-war with the strap of your case

† Tickle your toes as it blows warm air

The trunk of an elephant is one of the most versatile limbs on any living creature. It can delicately remove a tiny object from the ground, or be extended to grip and pull large branches from high in the trees.

Education of the Young

It was mid morning in Yala National Park. We watched across an open area backed by dry short shrubs, as a huge yellow grey elephant wandered into the clearing, her tiny infant darting in and out between her legs.

The mother stopped and became absolutely still. After a short time her little charge came and stood beside her, facing the same direction. Using her right front leg, the mother gently kicked a tuft of grass with her wide toe nails. As the tuft loosened, she curled her trunk around it, grasped it, shook it removing residual dust, placed it in her mouth and began to chew. Again and again she went through the same motions. The little one appeared to imitate. It kicked at a tuft, but missed and sent dust into the air.

With typical elephant patience, the mother repeated the process. Again the baby kicked up dust, its trunk darting in another direction. The mother continued to demonstrate but the baby retained its uncontrollable style.

Suddenly the mother turned and strode off toward the bushes. Hastily she tore some small branches from the shrubs and making a pile she clasped it in her trunk, approached the baby, dumped the pile directly in front of it and marched off.

An elephant must learn to use its trunk. The younger of these two babies appears to have found a useful model.

Tuskers are rare and always male. In Sri Lanka only ten per cent of male elephants grow the precious ivory.

Tusks

An elephant with tusks, a tusker, seems to know that he is rare, that he is special. With long, gleaming curves of ivory, gracing his anterior, he stands proudly, at times edging them forward as if to insist, ever so subtly, on his rightful attention.

Only a tusked elephant is given the honour to carry the Buddha's relics, the remains and possessions of the Buddha, in religious festivals.

The Pearl Within: Deeply embedded in some tusks is the *Gaja Muthu*, or 'Elephant Pearl'. Whilst actually dentine attached to a foreign object within the tusk, these *pearls* are to many highly precious and give an animal endowed with one an extremely high status. A tusker is sacred, but a *Gaja Muthu Atha* (tusker with pearls), is particularly auspicious. Some say the pearls ring like bells.

Sri Lankan Elephants and Their Tusks

† Tusks are actually extended teeth

† Only ten per cent of Sri Lankan male elephants have tusks

† Average length of a tusk is almost two metres

† Average weight of a pair of tusks is 35 kilos

† Largest recorded weight is 52 kilos (per pair)

† Shapes of the tusks vary. They may be short or long, curved or straight, thick or slim, vertical or horizontal. When curved, the tusks may vary in direction, or they may cross. Crossed tusks do not usually impede the elephant

† Tusks continue to grow throughout the life of the elephant

† Tusks consist of dentine. They contain about 45% calcium

† Mahouts call the tusks of young elephants 'cane tusks'

† Elephants may use their tusks to dig, to spar with their mates, to gore an enemy, to carry logs

† Some elephants have tushes, which are similar to small tusks. Whilst usually categorised separately in Sri Lanka, tushes are considered to be small tusks by some scientists

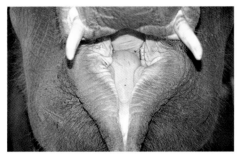

Many elephants produce tushes which some consider to be small tusks. Sometimes these tushes remain unexposed.

Ears

Whether curled or freckled, rounded, elongated or angular, the ears detect the myriad sounds, close and afar. Outstretched ears capture sound waves. Flapping ears function as a cooling system. It is in the ears that the veins of the elephant are closest to the surface of the skin. The gentle breeze created by the continual movement cools the veins and reduces body temperature. A minimal rise in body temperature, even half a degree, may result in increased ear flapping. Sitting atop an elephant, the rider feels this gentle breeze stirred by the serene and persistent motion of the ears.

The possession of an elephant with the right part of its right ear decayed will result in the death of the owner's sons. When the hind part of the left ear is decayed it will result in the death of the queen. Long ears, large broad and curled, when combined with other auspicious characteristics, bring wealth and prosperity.[62]

The caretaker of this magnificent tusker claims 'This is the biggest tusker in the world – sometimes'.

Feet

Of all footprints

That of the elephant is supreme. (Buddha)

Elephants move silently across the earth. On tip toes and well padded feet, which expand and contract, they amble at a slow pace and with a rhythmic gait. They can achieve a brisk stride or even a moderate run. Depending on the availability of food they may walk from 30 to 50 kilometres a day, and they can achieve a speed of up to 30 kilometres an hour.

So graceful is the elephant's movement that people may compliment a dancer with the statement, 'She moves like an elephant'.

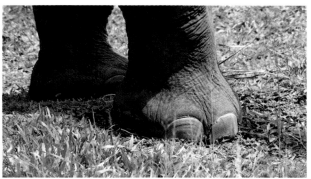

Above: Elephants move silently across the earth. On well padded feet they amble with a slow pace and a rhythmic gait.

Left: Some elephants clean their toe nails often, sometimes using another elephant as a platform.

Toe Nails

According to the ancient texts, elephants possessing 20 soft nails, shaped like the waxing moon, are to be preferred. Elephants with no nails, decaying nails or double nails should be *discarded immediately.*[63]

Most Sri Lankan elephants have 18 toe nails, four on each hind foot and five on each forefoot. Some however have 20, five on each foot. Many Sri Lankans believe that all their elephants have 20 toe nails, that Sri Lankan elephants are the only elephants with 20 toe nails and that this makes Sri Lankan elephants very special.

Clean shiny toe nails are a sign of a healthy elephant. Mahouts (elephant keepers) pay particular attention to toe nails. With their small sharp knife, they shave and clean the soles and nails. Some elephants take particular care of their toe nails. Raising their feet to rest them on an elevated platform, even another elephant, they wash and tend to their nails with their trunks.

Eight year-old Puja was standing ankle deep in a stream beside her mother Lakshmi. Beneath the ripples of the water, Puja's perfectly formed, broad white toe nails were visible. We commented on their beauty and as if she understood, she moved toward us, placing her right forefoot in front and bending her knee slightly, permitting us a better view of her toe nails.

Eyes

Kindness, gentility, tears and sadness,

Meditative states, old and wise,

Glints of audacity,

Smiles of conspiracy,

All live deep within elephant eyes.

The external section of the elephant's eye is comparatively small. Vision, which is limited to about 25 metres, may be easily dazzled.[64] This short sightedness improves in jungle areas and is well compensated by a highly acute sense of hearing and smell. According to the ancient texts, *Eyes like emeralds or golden in colour are to be preferred, but eyes continually watering are not favoured.*[65]

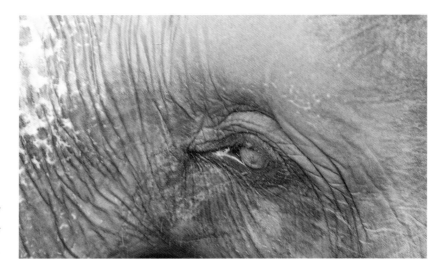

The outer section of the elephant's eye is comparatively small. Its vision is limited to 25 metres.

Tail

The tail may be long, short, straight, crinkled, spotted and splayed at the end with a hairy circumference. It makes an excellent fly swat. Walking tail to trunk is a practice adopted by elephants, some say for reassurance.

According to ancient texts, elephants were categorised into a caste system based on their physical attributes. An elephant with a long tail and abundant hair at the base will bring good fortune to its owner.

Whilst engaged in copulation, a bull elephant may be interrupted by an unwelcome competitor. The intruder has been observed to take hold of the lover's tail, and pull it, often dislodging the lower section, and leaving the aggrieved elephant minus part of his tail and possibly minus the satisfaction of a passionate encounter.

In Sri Lanka the short tailed elephant, *Walige Kota*, is treated with caution. Regarded as the loser in battles for supremacy, it develops unpredictable behaviour and may therefore be dangerous. Its short temper is said to complement its short tail.[66]

The hair at the end of the elephant's tail is considered to be especially lucky. It is often fashioned into a bracelet and worn for good fortune.

An elephant with trunk, penis and tail touching the ground is to be favoured. [67]

The Most Preferred Characteristics in an Elephant

Twenty soft nails of the toes, soft skin, long and slender trunk, eyes resembling Domba flowers, long and straight penis

O King, elephants possessing the above characters will bring you all prosperity and happiness. [68]

THREE

THE WAY
OF THE
ELEPHANT

ENIGMATIC CREATURES

*T*HE silence of the elephant bespeaks the silence of the watcher. For to stand in silence and observe even a single elephant is to render time motionless. It is to be transfixed by one of nature's most miraculous creations. These massively strong and highly sensitive creatures are the largest of all the animals that walk the earth. Their very being exudes a nobility and wisdom that is awesome and inspiring. Mystics and poets, prophets and gurus have embraced and celebrated the elephant as a symbol of all that is worth knowing and preserving. Perhaps this is because, in the presence of the elephant, we feel our own humility.

Whilst the Sri Lankan elephant has unique characteristics, its ways are, for the most part, the ways of all elephants. The extent of field research on the Sri Lankan elephant does not yet equal that undertaken in other countries. In this chapter we profile the way of the elephant drawing on the observations and research findings from other Asian countries and Africa, as well as from Sri Lanka.

Elephants Are Like Us

Elephants can be strong or weak, placid or rebellious, leaders or followers. They reach puberty at about the same age as humans, they move at about the same pace and, like humans, they live a life span of 65 to 70 years. They enjoy much affection and companionship. And, most significantly, they live in social groups that approximate the extended family unit. In describing the similarities between humans and elephants the wildlife biologist, Douglas H. Chadwick says:

> *For societies to operate at the bond group and clan level, each individual must be able to maintain preferentially close bonds with a large number of other individuals over an extended period of time. To do this...it helps to have a good memory for purposes of recognition, combined with good communication skills. And the key to fast, efficient communication is the ability to use a fairly sophisticated language. All of these characteristics both humans and elephants possess.*[69]

But whilst elephants are like us, the noted authority Carrington claims that we should actually be more like them. In his inspiring account on elephants he states that they:

> *...show affection and solicitude for mates that can well be held up as an example to members of our own species.*[70]

Herds

Elephants in the herd are intimately connected to each other in a rhythmic continuum of audio and tactile communication. It is through this collective cadence that the spirit of the elephants finds expression and the consciousness is informed.

Some claim that from the moment of conception, the unborn elephant is acknowledged by the herd with a wave of excitement. Certainly there have been observations of squealing and frenzied movements within the herd when the female rejoins her colleagues after mating. Throughout her 22 month pregnancy the expectant mother receives special attention from her mother, sisters, aunts and younger brothers. The baby she carries is not hers alone. It belongs to the herd. It is the future for her kin.

The newborn elephant is a miniature of majesty that is touched into being. With a unified curiosity the adults play their trunks over the tiny body of the new arrival. Every aspect of the baby becomes ingrained in the collective memory of the extended family.

Elephants in the herd are intimately connected to each other in a rhythmic continuum of audio and tactile communication.

Duty Statement for the Herd Leader

Matriarchs within the herd have derived their knowledge and expertise from their grandmother, mother, and aunts. They must be adept at many things.

In particular they must be able to:

† Command respect

† Offer guidance

† Delegate responsibility

† Identify good pasture and clean water

† Tolerate playful behaviour amongst the young (or even adults)

† Anticipate danger

† Execute appropriate survival strategies for a wide range of situations

† Encourage pubescent males out of the herd

The Matriarch: Whatever the elephant herd does, wherever it roams, it is guided by the largest and possibly the oldest female. As matriarch, her knowledge embraces many things. She knows where to find good pasture and clean water. She exercises discipline and facilitates co-operation. Supervision of birthing procedures and infant care are part of her responsibility. So too is the necessity to encourage the adolescent males to the periphery of the herd and beyond. This practice minimises in-breeding and ensures a robust species.

Lactating mothers, pregnant elephants, infants, developing adolescents and the elderly make up the several generations in the herd. The matriarch is sensitive to the unique requirements of each member. She seeks plants with appropriate nutrition. To avoid inferior or toxic foods that harm pregnant or lactating elephants she and her family browse on the lower areas of the mountains, leaving the higher areas with the smaller more toxic plants to the older males who are more tolerant to such foodstuffs.[71]

Survival of the herd is the motivating factor that guides the matriarch. There is safety in numbers. In the face of danger she may combine her herd with another. Babies will be forced to the centre; adults on the outside. At such times a straying infant will be quickly curbed by the sturdy tug of a huge trunk. For as long as is necessary the two (or more) herds will roam together while retaining their unique identity. At other times the matriarch might disperse her herd. When food is scarce, disbanding is prudent. The elephants have a wider choice and the environment is less damaged.

In a three year study of the Sri Lankan elephant by the Smithsonian Institution, George M. McKay observed the tendency of the herds to divide into a *nursing unit* comprising lactating elephants and infants, and a *juvenile care unit* of non-lactating adults and young. This arrangement benefits each group; the *nursing unit*, which is less able to travel because of the babies, and the *juvenile care unit*, which is free to move more quickly and over greater distances. There is much flexibility and interchange within these groups. However, even though they may share a common range with another herd, each herd retains its integrity.[72]

Over 100 years ago, when elephants were more numerous and roamed freely, Sir James Emerson Tennent, Lieutenant Governor of Ceylon, observed *the common lineage and relationship* within herds. He noted:

In a herd of 21 elephants, captured in 1844, the trunks of each individual presented the same peculiar formation, – long, and almost of one uniform breadth throughout, instead of tapering from the root to the nostril. In another instance, the eyes of 35 taken in one kraal [elephant round up] were of the same colour in each. The same slope of the back, the same form of the forehead, is to be detected in the majority of the same group.[73]

The herd then is no casual grouping of like-minded elephants. It is a complex and defined support structure of genetically related members, offering security, companionship and, above all, survival.

The herd is a complex and defined support structure of genetically related members offering security, companionship and, above all, survival. Whatever it does, wherever it roams, the herd is guided by the largest and possibly the oldest female.

The Silence of the Elephant

Perhaps it is the capacity for silence that is one of the most remarkable characteristics of elephants. Few who have observed elephants have failed to be touched by the sudden and silent appearance, not just of one but of an entire herd. They emerge as if from nowhere, as though they have somehow floated into view, materialising from the ether. Then, without warning and with the same characteristic silence, they make themselves utterly invisible.

Noting the silence of the elephants, Tennent stated:

> *When disturbed in the jungle, he will burst away with a rush...but the noise sinks into absolute stillness so suddenly...further search would disclose that he has stolen silently away, making scarcely a sound in his escape; and stranger still, leaving the foliage almost undisturbed by his passage.*[74]

Elephants are silent because they choose to be. If however they choose not be, they can generate sounds of such intensity that the earth vibrates. Intruders are warned!

We stood alone on the embankment. The elevated position enabled us to see across the dry parched earth, beyond the fence to the lush green crop.

Moments earlier two elephants stood on this same spot and viewed the same scene. Now their grey backs were just discernible above the green shoots of the sugar cane some 300 metres away. Their mahouts were in quick pursuit.

'Aliya! Aliya!', cried the mahouts, each raising his ankus head high.

'Aliya! Aliya!', they continued, as they gained distance.

Something moved our focus back from the wide view of the crop, back across the parched flat earth, back to where we stood. We were no longer alone. Forty elephants were standing with us on the embankment.

We stood stunned. How could 40 elephants surround us so quickly and so quietly? They were doing exactly as we had done moments earlier; watching their colleagues in the sugar cane.

Elephant Senses

Elephants have poor eyesight but they are highly sensitive to touch, sound and smell.

The eye of an elephant is small, compared to its overall body size. The positioning of the eyes allows substantial peripheral vision but the retina contains far fewer light-sensitive cells than a human eye. Vision beyond 25 metres is blurred.[75] In low light however, such as a forest, vision is less impeded.

Sound, touch and smell are the main senses by which an elephant guides its path through life. A blind elephant therefore will not necessarily be overly hampered.

Whilst their outer ear performs the all important function of a cooling system, the inner ear detects sounds, particularly low frequency infrasounds, over distances in excess of five kilometres. The importance of sound to the elephant has led Dr Deraniyagala, former Director of the National Museum of Ceylon, to speculate that deafness in elephants may be a factor in the foul temperament associated with 'rogues'.

By using its trunk to 'sniff the air' an elephant detects other elephants, creatures and people over some distances. Its capacity to smell is so acute, that it is able to distinguish particular elephants from others. It is also capable of sensing ground level vibrations either through its feet or trunk.

Elephants are often thought of as thick-skinned creatures. Indeed their skin can be as much as two centimetres thick. However they are highly sensitive to touch. They are irritated by a mosquito bite or a tick. They suffer sunburn. Working elephants are prone to blisters and infections from walking on hard road surfaces. Even a small stone lodged in the large padded foot can disable the elephant. Skin care is an important part of elephant life. The regular cycle of bathing and coating with mud and dust helps protect their sensitive coats.

Communication

It is easy when watching groups of elephants to imagine them deeply engrossed in the most intimate communication, to regard their gentle and extensive touching as the sharing of ancient secrets, their deep resoundings as an offer of wisdom, their squeals and rumblings as an expression of delight, and their trumpet as an early warning or perhaps part of a maverick game. Elephants are excellent and sophisticated communicators employing a myriad complex sounds and actions.

When elephants meet within or across family groupings, an intricate orchestration of sounds and movements occurs in what the noted authority on the African elephant, Cynthia Moss calls a greeting ceremony.

The two subgroups of family will run together, rumbling, trumpeting and screaming, raise their heads, click their tusks together, entwine their trunks, flap their ears, spin around and back into each other, urinate and defecate and generally show great excitement. A greeting such as this will sometimes last for as long as ten minutes. [76]

Cynthia Moss has spent many years studying elephants at Amboseli National Park in Kenya. She claims that at such ceremonies, elephants are maintaining and reinforcing family bonds. She regards greeting ceremonies as the epitome of the exceptional and special nature of the elephant.

I have no doubt, even in my most scientifically rigorous moments, that the elephants are experiencing joy when they find each other again. It may not be similar to human joy or even comparable, but it is elephantine joy and it plays a very important part in their whole social system. [77]

McKay's study of the Sri Lankan elephant reveals similar patterns of communication. He identified not only a complex range of sounds but distinct variations in the amplitude, quality and tempo of these sounds. Such differentiations significantly alter the messages communicated.

McKay identifies a distinct communication pattern between young elephants and adults. He describes a *long distance contact call used primarily by juvenile animals who have been separated from their groups.* As a response the adults issue a unique roar *similar to a small motorcycle. This latter call has only been heard used by females answering [the roars of their young].* [78]

Elephants also snort. The snort may be a command to the herd to halt, move or change direction. Snorting is produced by the rapid expulsion of air through the trunk. Such sounds are easily detectable. However, many elephant sounds are inaudible to the human ear.

In 1984, researcher Katherine Payne, working with a group of Asian elephants (in the Washington Park Zoo, Oregon, USA) discovered the use of infrasound as a means of elephant communication. [79]

The low pitch of infrasound is inaudible to human ears but detectable by elephants. Two thirds of elephant communication may occur through infrasound. The advantage of such communication for the elephant is that these sounds travel over distances in excess of five kilometres and are less impeded by rugged terrain.

In response to a low frequency message a herd of grazing elephants, even a widely dispersed herd, can act suddenly as a united force. At exactly the same moment the elephants will cease eating. Babies scurry beneath the adults and each elephant becomes utterly still save for their ears that fan out and their trunks that probe the air. Perhaps the signal they have detected was issued as a warning of imminent danger by a particularly alert elephant. Sometimes, following an 'all clear' the elephants may resume their grazing. If the danger does not pass the entire herd may silently and quickly vanish to safer ground.

It appears female elephants ready to mate emit low frequency sounds to distant males. Male elephants in musth, a time of heightened sexual activity, issue a range of infrasonic sounds. According to elephant expert Joyce Poole, such sounds communicate different messages to different elephants. They may be attracting the females who are ready to mate, while at the same time warning other males to stay away. [80]

Research into infrasound communication amongst Sri Lankan elephants remains limited but, according to Dr Jeheskel Shoshani, head of the Elephant Research Foundation in the USA, the findings from studies amongst African and other Asian elephants are likely to apply to *Elephas maximus maximus*.

Whilst elephants are generally accommodating and seemingly tolerant, a perceived threat may result in a range of behaviours and sounds including snorting, extended ears, raised head, kicking of dirt, a loud boom through the trunk and head butting another elephant. Such communication is most likely to occur between males. However, McKay did observe one instance of aggressive behaviour of a female toward a male.

As he moved toward the centre of the group, the largest female in the group (an animal we had named Big Fanny) turned and rushed toward him. The male turned and moved at a fast walk toward the forest, Big Fanny following. After about 75 metres Big Fanny returned to the group. Five minutes later the male returned to the group and again Big Fanny ran toward him chasing him about 150 metres.

Such aggressive interactions between males and females were not observed frequently. No instance of aggressive interaction was observed between females.[81]

Whether elephants are still and seemingly silent, or whether they are engaged in a vigorous flow of movement and sound, their behaviour invites conjecture. Research findings to-date have detected a fascinating communications system. But clearly there is much still to be learnt.

Elephants are excellent communicators employing a complex range of sounds and actions.

Elephant Memory

Elephant memory is difficult to define. Debate continues about elephant behaviour and whether it is a genetically coded response and/or conditioning and memory.

It seems though, that elephant memory is not merely the stuff of legends. Elephants appear to possess a remarkable aptitude for remembering. They especially remember other elephants, good waterholes, valuable locations, traumatic episodes and other significant experiences. Remembering other elephants is crucial to the complex patterns of family life and relationships. Observers frequently remark on the ability of each single elephant to recognise hundreds of other individuals.

Ian Redmond notes that memory plays an important role in the hierarchy of male elephants.

> *Male elephants indulge in frequent trials of strength called sparring. These mock fights serve to establish a hierarchy based mainly on size and strength. Because elephants have such good memories, they not only recognise the other males they come across but also know their relative social standing without having to fight to re-establish it whenever they meet.*[82]

Elephant memory is legendary and has inspired a rich tapestry of story telling throughout Sri Lanka. Mahouts and trainers often marvel at the way in which an elephant will recall particular movements or locations that it may not have used for a long time. And those who have spent years observing herds of wild elephants are often in awe of the ability of a herd to recall watering places and favoured feeding grounds after intervals of many years.

Intelligence

There is continued debate within anthropological circles as to the best criteria for assessing animal intelligence. According to two of the most accepted criteria, elephants are high on the scale. Their brain size as well as their employment of tools are indicators of intelligence.

The elephant brain is not only large but it continues to grow during the life span.

> *Most mammals' brains at birth are about 90 per cent of their adult weight. The majority of what the animals need to know to survive is already built in – hard-wired, largely instinctual. By contrast, in a human infant, the brain is only 23 per cent of its adult weight; for elephants, the figure is 35 per cent. Like humans, elephants are designed to learn most of what they need to know. The extended period of nurturing is part of that process, and they continue learning throughout their long lives. Their brain is highly convoluted – another measure of intelligence, which they share with humans, the great apes and dolphins. And they have the largest brain of all land mammals. It weighs four times as much as ours.*[83]

The other indicator of intelligence, the employment of tools to modify their environments and extend their physical capabilities, is frequently demonstrated by elephants.

> † An elephant may use a stone or a stick as a missile which it can hurl with astonishing speed and pin-point accuracy over distances of 40 metres

> † Elephants in captivity may use a stick in their trunk to extend their reach beyond the confines of their chains, enabling them to obtain otherwise inaccessible food

> † In the dry season, when rivers run low, elephants have been known to gather rocks and construct a dam, thereby raising the water level so they can drink or bathe in comfort

When loading logs, working elephants demonstrate a remarkable aptitude for symmetry and balance. Many stories attest to their skills in 'knowing' exactly how to place each log without upsetting the load. Indeed, many working elephants execute their tasks with minimal commands.

Water plays an important part in the life of elephants. It is essential to the cooling of their massive bodies and the quenching of their enormous thirst. But, above all, it is at the watering hole that elephants express their communal nature. It is here that herds mingle, babies learn to swim and females may issue invitations to a mate.

Elephants eat for approximately 18 hours a day. In this time, a full-grown elephant consumes from 100 to 200 kilos.

Musth

In Hindi the word musth means 'intoxication'. In Sinhala it is a derivative of the word *madha*, mad. An elephant in musth usually displays aggressive and unpredictable behaviour. The condition of musth is characterised by a thick pungent substance that oozes from the temporal gland between the eye and the ear. Muscles swell and the elephant's already poor eyesight is further diminished.

In mythology, musth was created by fate. Being divine creatures, the elephants were required to assist the gods and repel the demons. They became frightened and turned to Brahma for help. Musth was created in them to invigorate and infuriate them. In such a state they turned on the demons and defeated them.[91]

Musth first appears when the elephant reaches about 17 years. From then on the condition occurs annually in a healthy elephant. The intensity of the condition can vary dramatically depending on the nature of the elephant, its general wellbeing and whether it is wild or domestic.

In describing the severity of a drought, the Indian epic, *The Ramayana*, records that the Lankan elephants were so badly affected they did not come into musth.[92]

Musth lingers longer in domestic elephants and it can develop at any time of the year. With wild elephants it tends to be less pronounced.

Whilst barely discernible among females, for male elephants musth is a period of heightened sexual desire. Wild elephants in musth seek to establish their dominance amongst males. However, contrary to popular belief, an elephant does not have to be in musth to be sexually active. In 1957 Mr Sam Elapata Senior, Disawe (Governor) of Atakalan Korale in Ratnapura district was observing a group of wild elephants mating. Widely respected for his knowledge of elephant lore and known affectionately as Sam, the Elephant Man, he noted: *Above all none of the males was in musth – at any rate there were no traces of glandular secretion moistening the cheeks.*[93]

Owners of domestic elephants take particular care when their charge is in musth. Some claim that during this time the elephant is distressed and racked with pain. It must be secured for the duration. Its aggression is directed mostly toward those to whom it is closest. For this reason the usual mahout keeps both distant and silent, while care of the elephant is assigned to an assistant or to the mahout's family.

Musth is a time of heightened sexual activity. Confined almost exclusively to males, this condition results in unpredictable and aggressive behaviour. According to some owners, an elephant in musth is distressed and racked with pain.

It can be dangerous to get close to an elephant during musth. This hollowed log is used to pass food to an elephant in musth, thereby enabling the keeper to retain a safe distance.

Raja's Headache

He stood alone and apart on a grey slab of rock. And he stood below – below all who saw him. His patch was on the river bank. To be with him it was necessary to descend the steep embankment. But whether viewed from above or on the level, he formed the centre piece of a lush panoramic backdrop. His black form and slim, white tusks gleamed against the layered foliage and wide flowing waters of the *ganga*.

This was a scene of peace. And in some inexplicable way this elephant exuded peace. But he was not peaceful. His exaggerated movements indicated otherwise. He maintained a forceful and staccato sway. At times he would interrupt this, wrap the tip of his trunk into a tight ball and press it into his forehead, into the point from which moisture slowly oozed. Loosening his trunk, he would return to his forceful percussive movements, incorporating his trunk and penis as he thrust both under his body toward each other. He swung, he turned, he backed, always with force. But no place, no position seemed right.

These motions, so random and erratic, contrasted markedly to the normal fluid dignified movements of this elephant, Raja. This Raja is the prize of the Gunasekara family. He is revered and has on several occasions assumed the esteemed responsibility of carrying the sacred relics in the Kandy *perahera* (parade). Today he is at the mercy of these uncontrollable events which have stolen his composure, his decorum.

Raja is in musth. He has been in musth for three months. He is secured to his spot with chains. His only visitors, his owner and mahout, approach quietly. They keep their distance. From a distance he is sprayed with water. From a distance he is dispensed his food.

The normal intimacy between Raja and Mr Appuhamy, his mahout, is severed during this time. Closeness may spell danger.

Mr Gunasekara also looks on. 'Raja has a headache' he comments. There is no doubting his concern and regard for Raja. 'He's very intelligent. Once, when we were taking him to the Kelaniya *perahera* (near Colombo), he suddenly chased the mahout into a nearby house. I looked at Raja and asked him, "What are you doing?" He raised his trunk, went to a water tap and turned it on. He then went toward a car as if to damage it. I yelled at him to stop and commanded him to a nearby tree where he was eventually tied. I'm convinced he was trying to tell us that he was coming into musth and that we'd better do something before he became too dangerous'. Soon after Raja began musth.

Sri Lankans claim that an elephant in musth is most aggressive to its 'loved ones'. Should the usual mahout speak to the elephant during this period, the elephant may respond by throwing wood, attempting assault or trumpeting loudly. Eager to demonstrate this phenomenon, Mr Gunasekara instructed the mahout to break his silence and talk to Raja. And so Mr Appuhamy yelled, albeit reluctantly, at Raja.

But the expected response did not eventuate. If an elephant can look puzzled, amused and nonchalant, then Raja looked all of these successively. He would have nothing to do with such games. Mr Gunasekara looked amazed. 'I think Raja is coming out of musth' he said with delight.

Special ceremonies are held for elephants at the cessation of musth. For Raja, Mr Gunasekara lights a lamp and makes a vow for his continued good health.

Hora Aliya – The Rogue

A rogue elephant, *Hora Aliya*, roams alone, displays aggressive behaviour, strays into areas of human habitation, destroys property and may even kill people. However, not all lone elephants are rogues. Most loners roam peacefully, content with their own company.

It is difficult to say exactly why an elephant turns rogue. He may be the 'disgruntled' loser in the male battle for supremacy. He may be the victim of a destroyed habitat. Venturing into a village or plantation, he may have incurred injuries from bullets or traps. From then on he would know continuous pain. He would become increasingly anti-social and he would not be welcomed by other elephants. As his pain and alienation increase, so too does his aggression. And so begins a vicious cycle of violent confrontation between elephant and people.

Sankha's Story
Taming a Killer

He is probably 35 years old and three metres tall. His name Sankha, means prosperous. It is also a name given to a shell that makes a haunting sound when you blow through it. In some ways Sankha's life has become shell-like. On the outside his massive but gnarled body is testimony to countless onslaughts. His crumpled grey skin lacks the lustre of a spirited elephant. His trunk, though long and thick dangles as if in defeat. His shortened knobby tail is without grace and his toenails are now in decay. He looks older than his years and his weary gait suggests that for this elephant time weighs heavily. But his eyes reveal something beyond the exterior. Though tired and, at times, listless they proclaim an altogether different life. A spirited life that exists perhaps only in the recesses of his memory.

Today Sankha's home is a small park in the centre of the Kurunegala township in the North West Province. Seven hundred years ago this town was the royal capital of Sri Lanka. The giant rocks, *Atagala* and *Ateinigala* (he-elephant rock and she-elephant rock), dominate the region and dwarf Sankha's now diminished domain where the ghosts of past monarchs are said to linger. It is toward these rocks that Sankha gazes for many hours each day.

When he is not facing the rocks, Sankha is likely to be in his bath. That is where he seems happiest. Some say that is where he can forget.

But elephants do not forget. And Sankha still bears the scars that mark the end of his years in the wild and his extraordinary resistance to a life in chains.

For Sankha the only alternative to capture was death. The rapidly dwindling forest and increasing encounters with human settlements turned him into a rogue. He had killed 14 people and destroyed 200 properties by the time the wildlife authorities decided to take action. Allowing the elephant to remain inside the shrinking jungle was not feasible. Nor was translocation. The villagers wanted him killed. The official order to shoot the wild elephant was issued. But Dr Sarath Kotagama, the then Head of the Wildlife Department, had other ideas. So concerned was he about the dwindling elephant population that he recommended capture and domestication.

Sankha's freedom ended on 9 September 1990. After three weeks of successfully eluding a small army of wildlife officers, villagers and veterinarians he finally emerged from the thick jungle into a clearing near the side of the road. This was a most appropriate place for the tranquillising gun to be fired. The dart entered his rear end and the massive elephant was soon reduced to a crumpled grey heap on the dusty floor at the edge of the jungle.

Within minutes of tranquillising an elephant for capture, ropes must be fastened to the body and secured to a tree. The antidote to the tranquilliser must then be administered, allowing the elephant to stand and resume normal breathing. The moment it regains consciousness an unsecured elephant is a potential risk to the lives of the capture team and the nearby residents.

But the area where Sankha fell was denuded of all trees. He could not be secured. Perhaps he chose this clearing as a final act of defiance. For a while it seemed as if Sankha would have to be shot after all.

Salvation for Sankha came in the form of a bulldozer used to clear the very forest that once gave him shelter. The ropes were tied to the machine and the antidote given. He trumpeted continuously and tore with every muscle at the thick ropes as the bulldozer slowly edged its way along the road in search of a suitable tree.

Eventually a lone Palu tree was located. For the next few weeks that tree was Sankha's pivot in his transition from freedom to captivity.

'The lone elephant on the lone tree' was a term of affection coined by the villagers who could now burn their oil lamps at night without fear of intrusion from a four tonne marauding beast. Only days earlier, these people had wished the elephant dead. Now that they heard his screams and witnessed his vigorous yet futile attempts to sever the ropes that bound his legs, they wished him well. According to Dr Kotagama, the villagers knew in their hearts that it was they who had encroached on the elephant's territory. Perhaps the villagers also acknowledged the crucial role played by an elephant in the history of their region.

> *Following the murder of King Wathimi in the 14th century (he was pushed from the top of Atagala) the kingdom was without a ruler. The state elephant came to the rescue. In accordance with tradition the elaborately adorned animal was sent out to wander the district and select an heir to the throne.*

> *Not only did the elephant select a nobleman, but the man before whom the elephant knelt was the abandoned son of King Wathimi and therefore the rightful heir to the throne.*[94]

For several days the sympathetic villagers brought large quantities of food for the captured elephant. But Sankha refused all offers. Grabbing the food he would send the people scurrying as he flung it back at them.

Water was pumped onto his body to prevent dehydration. Still he refused food. His screaming rarely ceased and his relentless struggle with the ropes cut deep into his flesh. The wounds were becoming serious.

Meanwhile, the authorities were debating his future. It was decided to auction him. His purchaser would have the job of breaking him in and training him. Applications were sought and potential buyers came to view him. At the auction the highest bid was below that which would secure even a common buffalo. For Sankha this added insult to injury. An elephant cannot be valued below a buffalo. The idea of auctioning Sankha was dropped.

On hearing of the elephant's plight, the then President of Sri Lanka, President Premadasa, gifted him to the people of the North West Province. Care of the elephant became the responsibility of the Chief Minister of the Province and Mr Saman Senanayake, the Director of the Provincial Environmental Authority.

Sankha was untied from the lone Palu tree and coaxed into a huge truck for what became a painstakingly slow ten hour journey to the grounds of the Chief Minister's office in Kurunegala. The sight of the vehicle with the still protesting elephant drew a crowd of many hundreds.

On arrival, Sankha was again tethered. The festering wounds on all four legs and neck were now swarming with maggots. Immediate attention was required. Two bullets were found lodged in his body, a legacy of his conflicts with people. These would need to be removed. But Sankha would still not allow anyone close to him. A spray gun was used to disinfect the wounds. The neck wound was attended by a man, who directed the spray from high in a nearby tree.

It took nearly 45 days for Sankha's wounds to show signs of healing and even longer before the bullets could be removed. Finally Sankha accepted that his life had been saved on condition that he relinquish control to his human masters.

An early sign of his diminished resistance came when he accepted the pineapple that the Chief Minister brought each day. When a mahout climbed a nearby tree and stroked his back with a large brush of coconut fibre, Sankha protested loudly but only for a short while. He soon allowed the brushing to continue. And when Mr Saman Senanayake stood in front of Sankha and beat loudly on a Kandyan drum to acquaint him with unnatural sounds, Sankha became agitated. But the drumming continued and Sankha learnt to ignore it.

Then came time to introduce the ankus, the goad. With the help of tame elephants he was trained to walk to the command of the mahout. For Sankha this was not a problem. To stop him walking became the problem. But he soon learnt to obey. His regular walks along the road were always accompanied by a police escort and a curious crowd.

Sankha's transition to domestic life was not without some tragic confusion. One night the mahout became very drunk. He untied the elephant and let him go for a walk. By this time Sankha was sufficiently familiar with the conditions of his captivity to know that walking at night was forbidden. The mahout was yelling at him and threatening him with the ankus. Mr Senanayake heard the commotion. He observed tears rolling down Sankha's face. 'The elephant wanted to obey the mahout but he knew that the command was wrong'.

The mahout was dismissed immediately. Sankha's new mahout, Mr Gnanaratne, comes from a long line of mahouts. He and Sankha quickly forged a close relationship.

Teaching Sankha to lie down was almost impossible. Mr Gnanaratne speculated that Sankha was probably frightened of his wounds re-opening. But unless an elephant is lying down, a full veterinary examination cannot take place. In January 1993, nearly two and a half years after he was captured, Sankha finally lay down. Mr Gnanaratne was elated. Sankha was getting better.

Today the killer elephant from the jungle has achieved much popularity as the tame elephant of Kurunegala. Contractors bring 200 kilos of food every day which Sankha readily devours. And almost every day school groups come to visit and learn about the ways of the elephants.

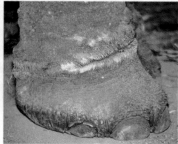

They say that Sankha is now like a baby. Certainly he looks placid. But as he sways continuously before the giant rocks, he exudes an almost definitive aloofness. It is as if his spirit remains elsewhere. Soon he will be adorned with a splendid cloth and he will learn to partake in the spiritual ceremonies of the people who captured him.

'I don't think elephants are really happy in captivity' says Saman Senanayake. 'But for Sankha it was that or death. We never hurt him, we only used love and kindness'.

Sankha received his name from Saman Senanayake. 'If I had a son that is what I would call him. I have a daughter. Sankha is like a son to me but I've tried not to become too fond of him because if I don't see him for a while, that would be painful for him and for me'.

In his home Mr Senanayake has a preserved foot from an elephant that was killed in the nearby jungles. 'I keep it for my daughter because I think that by the time she reaches the age of 50 there will be no more creatures like this in Sri Lanka'.

Competing For a Partner

In the wild, male elephants fight to establish their dominant position and to win the 'right' to mate. Sparring elephants are intriguing. Their behaviour was noted by Stanley De Silva, a contributor to *Loris*, the Journal of the Wildlife and Nature Protection Society of Sri Lanka. In the north east jungles near Polonnaruwa in September 1951 he observed:

> *The ears...fanned out...; then, coiling up their trunks they rushed at each other and met with a crash, the force of which vibrated through the very ground we stood on. We realised then that we were to be privileged but silent spectators in a battle between two wild bull elephants over the affections of a cow.*
>
> *The two bulls in this primeval amphitheatre continued to twist, push, heave and jockey for position. Occasionally one would deal the other a mighty blow with its trunk. Sometimes they would pause for breath, then back away slowly and cautiously only to hurl themselves at each other with redoubled speed and fury. At times one bull would beat the other to its knees and the hope of victory would kindle in its eyes. The other, by summoning all its strength, would repulse the attack. The battle between these titanic beasts went on for some time. Finally, one bull broke away under the furious onslaught of the other, and ran like a whipped cur into the jungle.*
>
> *Gasping for breath after its strenuous exertions, the victorious bull strutted up to the coy cow and caressed her with his trunk. The caresses were returned. After a few minutes the two of them moved off into a patch of jungle, apparently to continue their love making completely hidden from the eyes of man...'[95]*

On rare occasions, two bulls will fight to the death. Such a spectacle was witnessed near Polonnaruwa in 1989. The battle, between two evenly matched tuskers, continued for some days. Each tusker inflicted horrific wounds on the other. The sounds of tusks clashing was said to have been heard throughout the night over a great distance. Finally one elephant collapsed and died. The other returned to the jungle to 'lick his wounds'.

Elephant Mating

For elephants, successful mating depends on a confluence of factors, including healthy partners, a female in oestrus and a virile male. Oestrus, the time when a female may conceive, occurs annually and lasts for only two to four days. Even with the coalescence of essential factors, mating for elephants is usually not a haphazard or random act. Elephants are careful when choosing a sexual partner. Females will choose the strongest and most virile males. Who knows how they came to this knowledge? Maybe their revered matriarch has tutored them. Maybe it is instinct. But by suitable choice, the sturdiness and possible survival of the herd is ensured.

Females in oestrus make low sounds which males may identify from a distance of four kilometres. On approaching the herd the male detects the unique scent of oestrus females. He enters the herd and inspects potential cows. With care and precision, he explores their genitalia with his trunk. He then places his trunk in his mouth passing the genital substance onto an organ, known as the Jacobson's organ. Through this process he detects the sexual state of the female.[96] A female in oestrus may move from the herd. The male may pursue. For a time she may run freely while different bulls follow her. Finally she will curb her pace permitting one of the bulls to reach her. It is suggested that through this process she selects the sturdiest mate.

Mating elephants spend time 'getting to know' each other and they respect a certain protocol. Often the two link trunks, stroke and brush against each other. The female may present her rear to the male. The bull, standing behind her, lays his trunk on her back. As he mounts her, most of his weight is transferred to his hind legs. She emits low sounds. The act of consummation, where the one metre penis functions by way of a voluntary muscle, may take only a minute and is rarely longer than a few minutes.

Elephant mating may involve lengthy and complex rituals.

It can begin with the communication of sounds and smells over several kilometres.

On meeting, the elephants link trunks and caress in a prolonged exploration.

During mating, herd members often become spirited, squealing and moving in a lively fashion. After mating the female rejoins her herd and the male returns to his solitary life.

In Sri Lanka, the male has sometimes been observed to 'hang about' with his partner. Some say that he is waiting for confirmation of conception – only then will he leave.

The following description of wild elephants mating was made in 1957 by Mr Sam Elapata Senior.

The matings took place both on land and in water. One cow mated with two different bulls. A bull mated with two different cows and had five sexual connections with them in the space of an hour – the second three occurred in the space of ten minutes.

When the sexual act commenced the male placed his forefeet on the withers of the female; during the act the male's forefeet were gradually drawn backwards until at the end the male was standing almost erect on his hind legs. In each case the duration of the sexual act was about two minutes.[97]

In 1966 two elephants belonging to Mr Sam Elapata Junior displayed an attraction for each other. Kadira, the male, and Kapuri, the female, moved freely about Mr Elapata's garden. He wrote:

Kadira began fondling the female with his trunk. They moved from the sun toward the shade of the trees. As they reached the trees the male attempted to mount the female using a rock in the garden [to elevate himself]. Several attempts were made but all were unsuccessful.

...Kadira having attempted to mount about four or five times gave up and then they started fondling each other. They would touch each other with their trunks, intertwine them, put the tips of their trunks to each others mouths and caress each other in an almost human way. The female Kapuri kept on a constant rumbling noise which no doubt was one of affection. Kadira on the other hand used gentle pressure with his tushes starting from the head and going down gradually along the back right to the hindquarters. The pressure used by Kadira was by no means excessive but sufficient for Kapuri to feel and submit.[98]

Mr Elapata described a number of attempts by the male to mount the female. Finally, after a 'successful mount', the female trumpeted in what Mr Elapata concluded to be a cry of ecstasy. There were several more attempted unions between the two elephants over the next few days. Not all of them were successful. Unfortunately for Mr Elapata, and the elephants, the mating did not result in conception.

Professor Ratnasooriya's Findings

Through the captive breeding programme at the Pinnawala elephant orphanage, Professor Ratnasooriya, of Colombo University, and his colleagues have gathered valuable information on the oestrous cycle of the Sri Lankan elephant. In a paper he presented to the Sri Lanka Association for the Advancement of Science, Professor Ratnasooriya wrote:

We have established behavioural and hormonal data that the oestrous cycle in our elephants varies from 12 –16 weeks. The period when females are sexually receptive lasts for two to three days. During these days the female will stand and allow the male to mount. We observed various external signs associated with oestrous. The female becomes excitable and shows interest in males, rubbing herself on males and even on trees. A white gummy discharge appears from the urinogenital opening. The vaginal folds become swollen and the clitoris becomes visible. The vagina itself becomes reddish in colour. Males introduce the tips of their trunks into the urinogenital sinus of females in oestrous, frequently testing the urine. Usually this behaviour is seen at a rate of 12 times per hour but at oestrous it increases to 120 times per hour.

Intense urine testing by the male is indicative of attaining full receptive condition in the female. This is followed by precopulatory behaviour. Male and female engage in reciprocal touching behaviour of various parts of the body, especially of the mouth and genital regions. The penis then becomes fully erected. The male stands on his hind legs with forelimbs and trunk extended on the back of the female. The penis becomes s-shaped and about one third is inserted into the vagina. About four to nine pelvic thrusts have been observed. Ejaculation usually occurs about 30 seconds after intromission. Copulation lasts for one to two minutes. The male dismounts, but the couple remain in close proximity from a few hours up to three days, a pattern referred to as consort behaviour. Two to four copulatory episodes have been observed by us in a single oestrous day. A single female has been observed to mate with two males. Copulation was also observed in the river during bathing. Some females vocalise during mating. The reactions to copulation from other group members range from absence of any reaction to intense excitement including vocalisation, flapping of ears, urination and defecation.[99]

Pregnant Females and the Nursing Unit

Most females achieve sexual maturity between the age of ten and 12 years. They are capable of producing a calf every three to four years up to the age of 50. The rate and age at which the female produces depends on many factors including the availability and quality of food and her general health and wellbeing.

A pregnant female is rarely alone. At the time of her labour she may leave the herd to return later with her newborn. If she remains in the herd she will usually be assisted by her extended family.

Elephants have the longest gestation period of any animal on earth. For 22 months the female carries her baby. When born, it can weigh in excess of 100 kilos.

A newborn elephant is surrounded, even smothered, by love and support from a '*nursing unit*' within the herd. It can choose to suckle from its mother or several other lactating adults. Indeed it is a belief in Sri Lanka that when a baby elephant is born, seven female elephants come into milk.[100]

Babies in the Herd

In the national parks, it is easy to see baby elephants flanked by protective adults. In fact, regular observers have noted an increase in numbers of babies. Some people are optimistic. Such a presence may mean that the elephant population is expanding. However, others are more circumspect. They caution that when a species is on the verge of extinction, it may breed more quickly as if in a last ditch effort at survival.

Elephants have the longest gestation period of any animal on earth. For 22 months the female carries her baby. When born it can weigh in excess of 100 kilos. A newborn elephant is surrounded by affection and support from its herd. It may suckle from its mother or other lactating adults. There is a legend in Sri Lanka that when a baby elephant is born, seven female elephants come into milk.

The Birth of Puja

The hours linger painfully. Lakshmi sways her swollen body in a slow and exaggerated fashion. The motion may offer temporary relief for her labour pains. Sometimes her movement stops and she stands absolutely still as if meditating on the changes happening within her. Then the movement begins again.

She emits a low sounding groan, curls her trunk, presses it tightly into her forehead and holds it there for a long time as she shuts her eyes. Suddenly she opens her eyes and releases her trunk into a rapid almost violent swing across her underbelly. Occasionally she slaps a back leg against her vaginal secretions that now flow rather than trickle.

Her owner, Mr Sam Samarasinghe, and her mahout, Mr Dharmasena, have been with her since before sunrise. They utter reassurances. They stroke her and sponge her down to make her pain more bearable.

Mr Samarasinghe has waited a long time for this day when his elephant will give birth. It was two years ago that Lakshmi met Kandula, the working elephant who was captured in his youth from the jungles of Galgamuwa. Members of the Samarasinghe household were ecstatic when they heard that the meeting of the two elephants had been successful, and that Lakshmi was pregnant. People in the village were also excited. Lakshmi had acquired some status as a film star, having appeared in several documentaries and a feature film.

Lakshmi is kept more as a pet than a working elephant. Throughout the long months of her pregnancy she maintained the calm, serene temperament that makes her so popular with all who meet her. Sam Samarasinghe encouraged all who spoke to her to do so in dulcet tones. He was of the firm belief that a successful elephant birth requires peace and tranquillity in the mother.

The only change to Lakshmi's behaviour during that time was a developing fussiness with her food. She acquired a particular liking for one dish that was made especially for her. It consisted of soya beans soaked overnight in water, boiled and then pounded in a mortar to form a paste which was then moulded into balls. Throughout her pregnancy vitamin tablets would be inserted into these balls which she consumed with great relish.

In her first year of pregnancy she attended the Kandy Procession. Mrs Samarasinghe says Lakshmi looks forward to the festivals when she can be with other elephants. She seems to enjoy the music and the sense of occasion. The Kandy *Perahera* is looming once again but this year Lakshmi will not go.

Now her time has come. Mr Samarasinghe knows how precarious an elephant birth in captivity can be. He also knows that there is little he can do except be there, continue to offer reassurance and allow nature to take its course.

Suddenly Lakshmi trumpets. It is a high pitch trumpet, more of surprise than pain. Her movements become less agitated, more controlled. Then, like an expanding bubble, the white birth sac cocooning her baby slowly emerges.

Carefully synchronising the movement of her trunk and her hind legs, Lakshmi hastens her baby's arrival. The sac finally drops. Thirteen years of life, months of finding the right mate, 22 months of pregnancy and six hours of labour have resulted in this white blob on the ground.

Mr Samarasinghe rushes forward to assist the newborn. As if drawing open a curtain he pulls back the membrane to reveal a perfectly formed 64 kilo female elephant. It is late in the afternoon of 5 August 1986. Puja has now arrived into the world. Samarasinghe vigorously rubs the newborn elephant, as if massaging her to life.

Lakshmi takes an immediate interest in what she has produced. She wastes no time helping to clean the baby while exploring every inch of it with her trunk, a process that will imprint forever the identity of her offspring into her memory. At the same time she uses her trunk to lift the baby onto its feet.

Within ten minutes of entering the world, Puja is standing. She reaches a grand height of just 51 centimetres. There is ample room for her to position herself beneath her mother's forelegs where she quickly locates the source of the milk that will nourish her for the next two years. From day one Lakshmi develops a strong protective instinct towards her offspring.

Eight years later Puja is a healthy young elephant. She has clearly learnt the way of the elephants. Already she is a veteran of a number of festivals including the Kandy *Perahera*. In a few years she will be capable of bearing her own calf. Puja is at her most content when she is in the river next to her mother. To all who witness them, it is clear that this is one mother and daughter combination that will not be separated.

The bond between Puja and her mother is a talking point in the village. Once, when little Puja was being coaxed onto a truck for a 40 kilometre journey to a festival, she heard the familiar sound of her mother's trumpeting. Without hesitating, the young but determined baby elephant bolted out of the truck. She cast aside her ropes as she skipped towards her mother. No amount of coaxing would entice her back. The only solution was to allow both mother and daughter to walk together all the way to the festival.

Elephant Age

Elephants are born covered with wrinkles. Indeed it seems they are born old. Only against their elders is their innocence apparent. Their path to old age may be treacherous or easy. If they reach old age, about 70 years, they will be highly revered by the new generations.

The condition of teeth or molars is one of the best indicators of the age of an elephant. During its life-span an elephant will produce six sets of molars. These are like massive grinding stones that break down the fibrous intake. With its sixth set of molars, the elephant is in the final stage of its life.

A more traditional although less accurate method of determining the age of an elephant is to count the number of folds in the ears. As an elephant ages, the ends of its ears curl. One curl equates to about 25 years. Two curls suggest 50 years and, with the third curl the elephant is entering its last phase of life, somewhere between 60 and 75 years.

Wounded and Alone

Bundala Reserve is a small tract of coastal land in the south of Sri Lanka. The wet season had ended some two months ago. The land was already dry. The tracks were sandy and dust clouds in the trail of our jeep were slow to settle. The few large watering holes were dominated by wild wallowing buffalo and their faithful escorts, the white herons.

With their transfixed and serene gaze, the buffalo returned our stare. Sometimes one would heave its massive body out of the calm water, followed by another and then another. They never quite reached a stampede. Instead they would retreat for just a few metres, keeping their eyes firmly upon us.

We knew there must be some elephants around. We had sighted droppings less than a day old. The coastal vegetation was thick and three to four metres high, more than enough to conceal an elephant. We peered anxiously in all directions as we negotiated yet another track.

Occasionally a mongoose darted across the path. A large crocodile stretched out on a small island in one of the lagoons. And spotted deer scurried for some place else. The light was rapidly fading. In two hours it would be dark.

We arrived at a large open area flanked on the southern side by small sand dunes, a buffer from the ocean. We turned the jeep around for a panoramic view, turned off the engine and waited.

He appeared quietly from nowhere. He was alone. But unlike some elephants that roam alone, this one looked lonely. He moved with a flowing and deliberate gait across the open space toward the bushes. There he stopped, slapped his massive trunk on the ground and created a mini dust storm. Inhaling the dust, he sprayed his huge body. According to our guide this elephant was about 60 years old. He stood nearly three metres tall. We were soon to learn of the horrific trauma that plagues him.

We maintained our distance and watched. Suddenly clouds of dust and roars of engines moved in on the lone creature. Within seconds five jeeps laden with tourists vied for the best position to point their video cameras.

The drivers revved their machines and edged menacingly nearer. In spite of firm regulations, one eager tourist jumped from a jeep. With video camera in hand he stretched his arms full length to gain a few inches. With astonishing speed the massive elephant turned and raised his trunk high in the air, expelling a loud trumpet. With trunk still raised he headed toward the nearest jeep. He could so easily have crushed it and its occupants. Instead he paused. The frightened tourist scrambled back to his seat and the drivers frantically found reverse. The jeeps left more quickly than they had arrived and the lone elephant moved further into the bushes, blowing dust in his wake.

It was when the elephant turned around that we noticed the gunshot wounds. His ageing body was peppered with them. One shot had pierced his left eye.

Perhaps it was during the last dry season that he incurred his wounds. He possibly ventured into human habitation in search of water and feed. Perhaps he has been shot regularly for many years. No one could tell us. No one would know how many times this elephant had thwarted attempts on his life. Have other members of his family been killed? Has he become a rogue, pushed out by his family because the festering wounds have changed his behaviour? Has he killed people?

Against overwhelming odds, this elephant was a lone survivor. But what pain must he endure? And what memories does he hold? Now, as he is clearly finishing the final chapter of his life, alone and with very little sight, he is denied the peace and dignity that he deserves.

With the jeeps gone, he moved more slowly. We watched him disappear further into the bushes. Within moments he could not be seen. The shaking of the tree tops told us that he was still there finishing his meal. Soon even the trees became still.

Elephants and Death

Many observers claim that elephants have a concept of death. Cynthia Moss notes:

> *Unlike other animals, elephants recognise one of their own carcasses or skeletons. Although they pay no attention to the remains of other species, they always react to the body of a dead elephant.*[101]

Like Cynthia Moss, Iain and Oria Douglas-Hamilton have observed and written extensively on elephants.[102] The unique behaviour displayed by elephants around the death of their own kind attracts particular attention by the Hamiltons who have noted attempts by elephants to bury their dead and even remove tusks from the corpse.

In documenting the death of a female elephant within the herd, writer and naturalist, Marcus Schneck noted the way in which other members of the herd attempt to help the fallen female to her feet. They persist in their efforts until there is clearly no life left in the female. They will then continue to feed nearby, albeit in a *restless and uneasy way*.

> *While the body decomposes and its flesh is reclaimed by the earth over the next several weeks and months, any elephant that passes within scenting range is likely to divert its path to move near the carcass and to touch it. And, for years to come, elephants chancing upon the sun-bleached remains will stop to carefully examine the bones in a strange silence.*[103]

Elephant Graveyard

The legend of the elephant graveyard is a universal and apocryphal tale. Tennent tells of Sinbad of the Sea from the *Arabian Nights*. On his seventh voyage to Ceylon Sinbad was shipwrecked on the island. Sold as a slave he became embroiled in hunting for ivory. During a mishap he was carried away by an elephant and *he found himself amongst the bones of elephants and knew that this was their burial place.*[104]

Tennent learnt of the widely held belief in Ceylon in the existence of an elephant graveyard from a Kandyan chief. According to the chief, the final resting place for elephants was beside a clear lake in the Saffragam valley, deep in the mountains east of Adam's Peak.[105] This belief is still held by some.

However, scientists claim that there is no elephant graveyard. They advance a biological explanation for the fact that many elephants may die in one place. Once the final set of molars begin to wear, elephants are no longer able to chew the much needed fibre in their diet. This marks the onset of old age. At this stage, many elephants gravitate to areas where the plants are more easily chewed and where water is readily available. This is where they die.

The idea that it is more than simple biological necessity that drives elephants to a final resting place, that perhaps they are driven by some spiritual force, is generally accepted as myth. Why then do such eloquent stories persist? Maybe the imagining of an unexplained ritual enables us to cope with notions of death, especially amongst such revered creatures; and especially when the deaths have become more widespread through our own actions!

The Herd at Handapanagala

An abundance of fresh droppings and the occasional crack of a twig or rustle of a leaf told us that the elephants were not far away. We clambered quietly to the top of a rock. Peering into the dense scrub, we could just make out their grey bulk. Or were we staring at other rocks? Perhaps the elephants sensed our presence. Within seconds, and in absolute silence, they vanished.

We waited. Our raised position gave us a vantage point. But the fading light and dense scrub made visibility difficult.

Suddenly the air was wrenched apart by a deafening and reverberating trumpet. Beneath us a small black elephant, with raised trunk and thin white protruding tusks, darted across the clearing. Hot on his heels were two huge elephants. The disturbance ended as quickly as it had begun; perhaps the result of effective parental discipline. Silence returned. No sign of the elephants remained.

To minimise further trespass on elephant territory, we walked quickly and quietly in a wide circle to the mudflats at the edge of the tank (an ancient constructed lake).[106] A large herd of wallowing buffalo watched us emerge from the scrub. One of them snorted, then bolted into the water. Its actions triggered a stampede that transformed a picture of serenity into chaos. This would surely alert the elephants to our presence.

Finally the buffalo settled. We moved around the perimeter of the tank and waded ten metres to a small island where the trees, boulders and low scrub made an excellent camouflage.

Now downwind of the elephants, we squatted and waited as we scanned the panorama before us. Across the water to our left was another much larger island formed by massive boulders, stacked precariously. In front of us, across the water, was the dry grey understorey of the forest. There, the elephants were waiting.

Some minutes later the white herons took flight. The buffalo slowly backed to one side. Did they sense that something was about to happen?

Without warning a large elephant appeared in front of the dense scrub. She moved to within a metre of the water's edge. Apart from the occasional flap of her ears she remained totally still. Time passed. Still she did not move. But one sensed a purpose in her stillness. After ten minutes she began to swing her trunk, gently stirring the dust at her feet. Then raising her trunk she positioned it above her head as if to survey the scrub behind her.

A second large elephant with a young tusker appeared from the bush. They stood together, the tusker flanked by the two adults. He was just too big to fit under their bellies. The three walked toward the water but the tusker hesitated. As the adults moved forward he fell behind. Grasping his trunk in hers, one of the adults pulled him toward the water. But the tusker resisted. Pulling back he freed himself, his tiny trunk flung into the air. The large elephant tried again but in vain. The two adults then turned and walked tail to trunk, swaying gently along the mud flat.

The tusker stayed by the water's edge watching. He did not venture in.

By now another three adults and one baby had emerged from the scrub. They stood, as if in conference, near the tusker. More groups began to appear from the bushes. After 30 minutes over 20 elephants stood on the mud flats. One of them approached the buffalo, slowly at first but then quickening to a run. The buffalo fled with a boisterous spraying of water.

Now the mud bank belonged to the elephants. Over 50 of them linked trunks, clutched tails, blew dust and rubbed heads. Some were particularly frisky, others seemed deep in meditation.

The peace and tranquillity were suddenly shattered by the distressed snorting of a young buffalo that had become separated from its herd. Bellowing, it ran full pace across the mud flat. Most of the elephants appeared totally nonchalant. But one large female made a sweeping action with her trunk as if to hurry the youngster along.

Once again a quietness descended.

Having walked the distance of the mud flat, the first two elephants returned to the little tusker. Another attempt was made to coax him into the water but again he resisted. One of the adults moved slowly behind him. Lowering her head she gave a quick butt to his rump. The little one squealed and turned, moving away from the water. The two adults watched for a moment, then facing the water they entered with a deliberate almost defiant march. Now was the time for bathing and drinking. One by one each elephant followed the leaders into the water. Except for one; the little tusker who stood very still and watched.

One large female with two larger male consorts moved to a corner of the tank. They stood still as three points on a triangle and exchanged glances. As she approached one male the other moved away. She stopped, turned and observed the departing figure. He was the one she wanted. She caught up with him further into the water and immediately they began a lengthy caress. The first male wandered off, out of the water and back to the bushes, not with the usual fluid gait of an elephant, but with his head lowered and his trunk still. He stood inert before a large tree as the female continued her play with her chosen male.

The rest of the group converged to the centre of the tank. Above the still water their bulky backs, domed heads and swirling trunks formed an intertwining rhythmic mass. Every few minutes trunks would rise high into the air and lavish showers upon the herd.

One large male stood ankle deep in the shallows. He lowered his massive penis until it too was partly submerged. For some time he stayed in that position. Tentatively at first he ventured deeper into the water. Now, almost completely submerged, he swam swiftly and easily toward the group.

Within minutes he had merged into the rhythm of the performance he had been watching. He placed his trunk on the back of a large female, stroking her and nuzzling in toward her. She raised her trunk and released a shower of water. For some time they continued touching and caressing. Then the female submerged herself. Without effort her companion placed his forefeet gently on her back. He raised his head, straightened his colossal frame, and for some moments stood proud and statuesque.

Relaxing his stance he re-submerged himself into the water. The female surfaced, released a soft grunt and raised her trunk, creating another shower. The water cascaded like a stream of crystals over both of them.

The male hoisted his trunk, bending it slightly toward hers. As the waters from her trunk ceased, she mirrored his stance. The two trunks now created a perfect symmetry against the soft early evening sky. They lingered for just a moment. Then with utmost precision the tips of the trunk fingers drew toward each other and for an instant they met.

During the love making there was a quickening in the pace of the herd. Perhaps they had all been aroused. But now, as one cohesive group, they turned and swam toward the other island. The little tusker, still at the water's edge, rushed forward and began to swim after them. His small body struggled through the water. He made slow but steady progress.

It took only 15 minutes for the herd to reach the island and ease their massive bodies onto dry ground. The sheer blackness of their skin shimmered in the late afternoon sun. For a while, they seemed to merge with the giant boulders. In single file they contorted their bodies to an almost vertical position and scaled the steep terrain.

On top of the island they rubbed themselves against the trees. Their blackness soon turned to grey as they tossed dust over themselves. Now, slightly apart but still close, they began their evening meal. Moments later, just on sunset, they had all but disappeared.

We counted a total of 56 elephants, including ten youngsters. This is just less than half the number that live in this small confined area.

The daily ritual of these elephants is played out in a peaceful sequence that somehow belies real time. The serenity and tranquillity of their movements masks the urgency that underpins their very existence. This is a pocketed herd. Their former 18,000 hectare domain has been reduced to 60 hectares. Their freedom is bound by those who have trespassed their land. Electric fences, ditches, hidden spikes and sometimes bullets are used to keep these elephants away from development and plantations. 'Unless something is done soon, I'll give this group ten years', said Dr Kotagama, former head of the Department of Wildlife Conservation.

Each day, just before sunrise, these elephants come to the Handapanagala tank to drink, bathe, and sometimes mate. The serenity of this scene masks the urgency of the elephants' plight. What was once their 18,000 hectare domain is now reduced to 60 hectares. Electric fences, ditches, hidden spikes and bullets are used to keep this herd away from plantations.

A Status Attained

...When any other king or raja has one of these elephants of Ceylon, if they bring any other breed before them, in any other place whatever, so soon as the elephants behold the Ceylon elephants, by an instinct of nature, they do them reverence, by laying their trunks upon the ground and raising them up again.[107]

These observations were made by Jean Baptiste Tavernier, the 17th century French traveller and trader. Such sentiments of the superiority of the Sri Lankan elephant have echoed through the centuries.

Indeed the High Priest, Venerable Davuldena Nanissara Thero offers a basis for such a belief.

When the elephants were created they were divided into 12 castes. The highest caste came to Sri Lanka. All the elephants of the world, recognising and acknowledging the highest status of the Sri Lankan elephants therefore honour and revere them by prostrating before them.[108]

Many observers dismiss such notions. However, it cannot be denied that from ancient times to the present day, Sri Lankan elephants have been perceived as superior and therefore favoured for war, work and ceremony.

The way of the Sri Lankan elephant is clearly the way of all elephants. But in some inimitable way, *Elephas maximus maximus* has imbued the hearts and minds of many with a notion of something that is distinctive.

FOUR

WAR
SPORT
AND
WORK

THE INHERITANCE
OF THE ELEPHANT

*T*HEY say that deep within the eyes of the elephant you can glimpse the tragic mirror of history. Reflected there is a profound forlornness. This they say is the grief of their ancestry; the burden of knowing how many of their kin have perished for the wars, for the work, and for the folly of man.

For thousands of years elephants have been lured into pits or compounds. They have been separated from families, lassoed to trees, and instilled with abject terror. For many, capture resulted in physical and psychological wounds that would not heal. For the ones who fought courageously and relentlessly to save their kin, capture meant death. Some elephants put up little resistance. They went quietly with their captors. And quietly they lay down and died. Other elephants demonstrated such cunning that they were able to outsmart the men with ropes. They escaped back to the jungles for a few more months, or maybe years, of freedom.

As well as capture there was slaughter. Some called it sport. Full grown elephants would protect their young as men aimed their rifles. It was hard to miss. Trumpeting their agony the big creatures swooned as the bullets penetrated their eyes, tore their trunks, ripped their shoulders and pierced their brains. Some elephants escaped with hideous wounds. For years they would nurture the pain until the last vestiges of life finally ebbed from their broken frame, or until they once again faced the barrel of a sportsman's gun.

These then are the experiences that elephants know. This is their inheritance. That the elephants are such willing servants, that they are able to adapt so quickly from a spirited and free life of roaming the forests to a dispirited and deprived life in chains, may be a testimony to the superiority of those who imprison them. But it may also indicate the unfeigned co-operative nature of the world's largest land mammal and its innate willingness to survive.

Because the Sri Lankan elephant was favoured for war and for work, a viable export as well as domestic market rapidly developed. The ancient Sinhalese text, *The Mahavamsa*, contains many references to the use of elephants. Throughout the centuries, indeed from the time of the first Punic War,[109] traders, ambassadors, historians and travellers have spoken of the unique strength and intelligence of the Sri Lankan elephants and of their capture and export to India, the Middle East and other more distant ports.[110]

Later within the Kandyan Kingdom, elephants became the property of the crown.[111] To capture or slaughter them without permission was a serious offence punishable by execution. At least some of the executions would have been carried out by an elephant under the command of a mahout.[112]

Stories of elephant capture in Sri Lanka have become integral to the legends of the nation. Without the enforced labour of captive elephants it is unlikely that the island of Sri Lanka would have developed so rapidly in trade and commerce.

Traditional Capture – Method of the Pannikers

Before colonisation in the 16th century elephants were obtained largely through individual capture. This job, demanding extraordinary prowess and skill, fell mostly to the Pannikers, a group of Muslims from the east coast. These people maintained their skills and knowledge through generations. Descendants of the Pannikers exist to this day, although changed laws, modern technologies and a severely diminished elephant population have rendered their skills virtually redundant.

The Pannikers displayed a detailed knowledge of elephant behaviour and movements. Their only tool was a seven metre rope made from deer or buffalo hide.

Their methods involved sneaking up on an elephant and seizing the moment when the elephant raises its hind leg (something elephants often do) to attach the noose. The other end of the rope was quickly tied to a nearby tree. If no tree was available, the Panniker would run with the elephant in an attempt to entice the raging beast to a suitable position.[113]

In another method of capture, the noose was spread on the ground, concealed with leaves and earth and fixed to a large rock suspended from a nearby tree. This acted as a counterweight. A pit was dug which the elephant would see. In avoiding the pit the elephant was forced to step on the concealed noose. The weight of the rock would prevent the elephant from running away until the Pannikers could secure the rope.[114]

Once the captured animal was secured a shelter was erected to protect it from the sun. The taming and the training was begun almost immediately.

Prior to venturing into the jungle to catch elephants the Pannikers would observe complex rituals in order to placate the demons.

> *Though they call themselves Mohammedans and observe the precepts of the Koran, they are also devil-worshippers. No elephant catching expedition is entered on, till the five forest demons, male and female, feared by all jungle villagers, have been duly propitiated by ceremonies and offerings. Every day, while the expedition lasts, before the party starts to look for elephants, a coconut is broken at the edge of the forest and offered to the demons with supplication for success.*[115]

Mr Sharker Mohideen who now lives in Colombo has spent years in the jungles and has written on his observations of the Pannikers and their work.

Having secured the elephant the Pannikers will retire a short distance and keep watch. The victim...will tire in a few hours...[Some] 12...hours later, one or more of the men will approach the elephant with a large bucket of water which is placed so that the elephant can suck in the water by stretching his trunk. Hours later the man gives the elephant more water. The next day, leaves...will be offered to the animal, [These] will be devoured by the hungry elephant. This [process] will be repeated by the same man and the elephant recognises him as his saviour...There is now hardly any tugging of the ropes that bind the elephant's rear legs. A few days later, two trained elephants with their mahouts will approach the animal,...and gently press his flanks.

The mahout will slip off the back of the trained elephant and sit on the back of the captured animal. When they notice the animal is quiet the pressure is relaxed, the ropes are loosened and the elephant is coaxed to walk along between the trained elephants. As a precaution, a thick chain is placed between one front leg and the rear leg on the same side. This will prevent the animal from running.

The wound caused by the rope cutting through the skin and flesh is treated by a special ointment that the Pannikers prepare...The man who first watered and fed the animal will continue to do so. Sometimes a heavy chain is wound around the neck together with a length of 'charmed' twine. Within a week to ten days the animal learns to accept the mahout on its back.[116]

Yet another method of capture was to use tame female elephants as decoys to lure males from the jungle to a spot where the Pannikers could attach the ropes.

Such practice raises the question of why a tame elephant would allow a wild one to be captured. Given the intelligence of elephants surely the tame female would warn the unsuspecting male of the fate that awaited him. This question may have been considered over a thousand years ago. In the ancient Indian epic, *The Ramayana*, elephants were recorded to *complain that they do not fear fire, weapons or spears, but they do fear their own selfish relations.*[117]

The Elephant Kraal – Ath-gala

He screamed in his anguish with his proboscis raised high in the air, then, falling on his side he laid his head to the ground, first his cheek and then his brow, and pressed down his doubled-in trunk as though he would force it into the earth; then suddenly rising he balanced himself on his forehead and his forelegs, holding his hind feet fairly off the ground. This scene of distress continued some hours, with occasional pauses of apparent stupor, after which the struggle was from time to time renewed abruptly, as if by some sudden impulse, but at last the vain strife subsided, and the poor animal stood motionless, the image of exhaustion and despair...The rest of the herd were now in a state of pitiable dejection, and passed closely together as if under a sense of common misfortune.[118]

This is how Tennent described the struggle of elephants captured in a 19th century kraal in Sri Lanka.

It was the Portuguese who perfected a method of catching an entire herd of elephants. The Dutch and then the English refined the technique. Known as the kraal, the technique involved the construction of a large enclosure to trap elephants.

The demands for elephant labour increased dramatically with the clearing of land for plantations, the building of roads and railways and the erection of large public buildings. Given that the capture of individual elephants was time consuming and that breeding in captivity was rare, a more efficient method of capture was needed. The kraals proved to be highly effective in trapping large numbers of elephants.

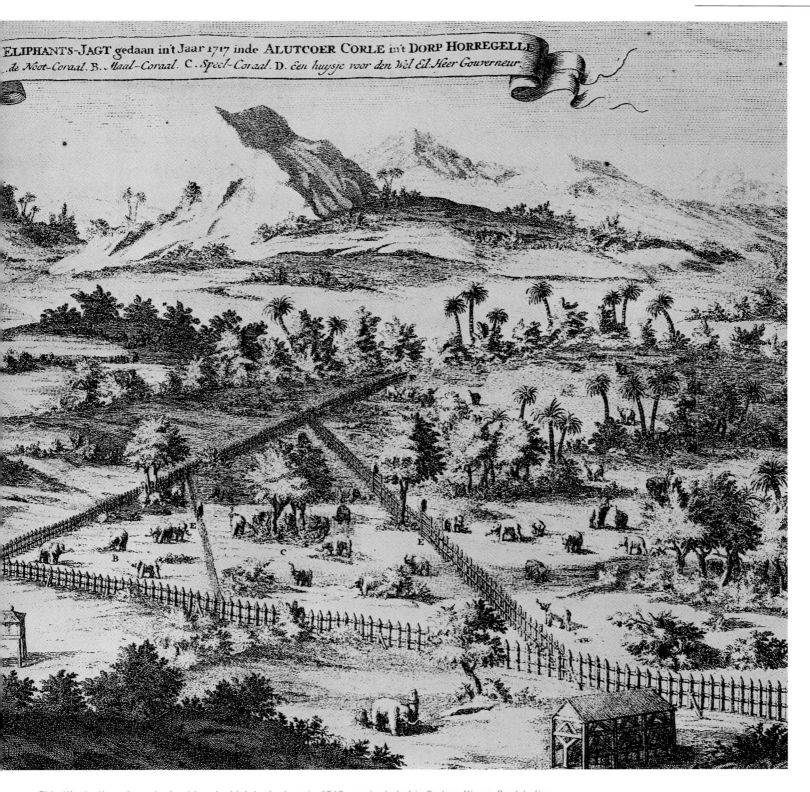

ELIPHANTS-JAGT gedaan in't Jaar 1717 inde ALUTCOER CORLE in't DORP HORREGELLE
.de Noot-Coraal. B. Maal-Coraal. C. Speel-Coraal. D. een huysje voor den Wel Ed. Heer Gouverneur.

This illustration of an elephant kraal which took place in 1717 was included in Oud en Nieuw Oost-Indien,
the manuscripts of Francois Valentijn, Minister of the Dutch Reformed Church.

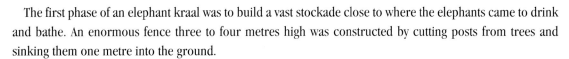

The first phase of an elephant kraal was to build a vast stockade close to where the elephants came to drink and bathe. An enormous fence three to four metres high was constructed by cutting posts from trees and sinking them one metre into the ground.

Cross beams were fastened with jungle rope made from coconut fibre and supporting beams were anchored to the outside to prevent the structure collapsing under the pressure of charging elephants. At the main entrance the vast sliding gate could seal the enclosure within seconds.

The size of the enclosure varied. As many trees as possible were contained within the fence as tethering posts for the captured elephants. The entire structure was then camouflaged with layers of foliage. At particular vantage points outside the fenceline, viewing platforms were erected for the many dignitaries who came to observe.

The early kraals were constructed by enslaved labour under a system called *Raja-Kariya*. This system was part of a complex feudal service developed during the time of the Sinhalese kings. It continued under the rule of both the Portuguese and the Dutch. It thrived under the British until it was abolished in 1832. Following the cessation of enslaved labour, kraals were built with the eager labour of volunteers. Such was the status of being a participant.

Once the structure of the stockade was complete other preparations could begin. Special ceremonies were held as a prelude to the capture. Priests would dance and chant through the night and well into the next day in order to seek protection from the gods. Sometimes the ceremony would include a dramatisation of the coming event. People acting as elephants and their captors would perform in ritualistic preparation.

The element of surprise was a crucial factor in diverting a herd from its path into the stockade. But first the herd had to be located. This was done by hundreds of 'beaters', mostly peasants who carried sharp pointed sticks, flares and even muskets. Their job was particularly arduous. They might search for many days and nights. Often they were far from home and they survived on barely adequate rations. They had to remain in absolute silence until a herd was sighted.

Following a sighting a signal was given, usually after sunset, and the forest exploded with rifle shots, flares, drums and hundreds of shouting people. Blinded by fear and desperate to escape the chaos, the wild elephants edged slowly forward and into the darkness of the stockade.

During one particular kraal observed by Tennent, the first attempt to drive the herd into the compound failed. A wild pig ran across the path of the lead elephant, causing the entire herd to swing away from the stockade and re-enter the jungle. Further efforts at capture were postponed until dusk.

The crowds of spectators maintained profound silence, and not a sound was perceptible beyond the hum of an insect. On a sudden, the stillness was broken by the roll of a drum, followed by a discharge of musketry. This was the signal for the renewed assault, and the hunters entered the circle with shouts and clamour; dry leaves and sticks were flung upon the watch fires until they blazed aloft and formed a line of flame on every side except in the direction of the kraal which was studiously kept dark; and thither the terrified elephants betook themselves followed by the yells and racket of their pursuers...They approached at a rapid pace, trampling down the brushwood and crushing the dry branches, the leader emerged in front of the kraal, paused for an instant, stared wildly around and then rushed headlong through the open gate followed by the rest of the herd.[119]

The second attempt resulted in the trapping of nine elephants, including two babies and a massive rogue.

> *Some, in their struggles made no sound, whilst others bellowed and trumpeted furiously, then uttered short convulsive screams and at last, exhausted and hopeless, gave vent to their anguish in low and piteous moanings. Some, after a few violent efforts of this kind, lay motionless on the ground, with no other indication of suffering than the tears which suffused their eyes and flowed incessantly.*[120]

Inside the stockade the elephants would form a tight circle with the young ones wedged firmly between the legs of their elders. According to Deraniyagala this formation rotated like a wheel.[121] The beaters would line the perimeter and use their sharp sticks to keep the captives away from the fence while flute players serenaded the bedlam. To the sweet strains of the music some elephants stood still, projected their ears and extended their trunk in the direction of the instruments.

Witnesses have often commented on a sense of order within the pandemonium, as if the elephants were co-ordinating an escape strategy. But with the gate shut, there was no way out.

With the herd inside the kraal, mahouts on tame elephants and men with nooses would enter. Many of these men wore specially charmed oils and uttered ancient incantations said to calm wild elephants.

The tame elephants would attempt to break the circle of wild elephants by isolating a single captive. The noosers would then tether the wild elephant to a tree. This risky job demanded great strength and courage.

Once tethered some elephants became perfectly still. Others however continued their struggle for many hours.

A common behaviour of elephants in the kraal was to emit steaming vapour. Deraniyagala surmised that the vapour may have resulted *from heavy endocrine gland secretion induced by terror*.[122]

During the noosing the baby elephants would dart frantically from one female to another, seeking comfort and reassurance between the legs of the larger animals. Tennent described one baby that offered extraordinary resistance to any attempts to noose its mother. It continually placed itself between its mother and the noosers making relentless efforts to grab the rope while lashing out with its still undeveloped trunk. Finally the baby had to be driven back. Once the mother was noosed and tethered the baby returned to her side and charged anyone who passed. Eventually it too was noosed to a tree.

Use of Tame Elephants

The courage and sensitivity of the tame elephants (also known as monitor elephants) in the kraal has become legendary. In their role to calm the wild elephants they rarely inflicted injury. Amidst the pandemonium they maintained the safety of the mahouts on their backs and the noosers on the ground. These tame elephants had once been wild themselves, trapped by a kraal perhaps only months earlier.

If a wild elephant became particularly unruly the tame ones would instinctively flank it and, with some force, encourage it toward a tree where it would then be secured. Instances of tame elephants sustaining injuries from wild elephants struggling to break free were rare.

Death in the Kraal

Death and serious injury amongst the wild elephants was not uncommon within the kraal. Some would be crushed in the panic. Others died from the horrific flesh wounds resulting from their unfailing resistance. And, according to Tennent, some died seemingly from a broken heart. Such was the case with the lone bull that entered a kraal in 1847. This poor creature remained an outcast even within the stockade. It made repeated attempts to join the captive elephants as they formed themselves into a protective circle with the young ones in the centre. But the bull was always rejected. The rules that applied in the wild outside the stockade, remained intact within its walls.

After all the others had been noosed, the attention was turned to this bull. Immediately after noosing he became noisy and violent. But he soon lay down peacefully. According to Tennent, hunters believed that such behaviour meant the elephant knew that his death was imminent. For 12 hours the bull covered himself with dust, moistened with his own saliva. Eventually he stopped doing even this. He lay very still and died quietly.[123]

Elephants trapped in the kraals were sold at auction. Their destiny was usually to join the ranks of forced labour. Some of the luckier elephants were assigned to temples and had an easier life.

The numbers of elephants trapped in a kraal varied dramatically over the decades. In 1681, three different kraals captured 13, 104 and 204 elephants respectively. A kraal in 1779 succeeded in trapping 400 elephants. In the last kraal in 1950, 18 elephants were captured.

Opposite: Panamure elephant kraal, 1944. Painting by Dr P.E.P. Deraniyagala.

From the Dutch Diaries

Some of the diaries of the Dutch administrators offer a unique insight into the practices and problems of capturing and exporting elephants in Ceylon, as illustrated by the following example:

Memoir of Thomas Van Rhee, Governor and Director of Ceylon for his successor Gerrit De Heere. 1697

The capture and Sale of Elephants being the chief source of revenue to the Company in Jaffnapatnam, must be carried on with all assiduity, and requires every attention. With a view to encourage the hunters more, the Honourable the Commissioner Hendrick Adriaan Van Reede (of blessed memory) had arranged that for every elephant which is delivered above the tribute to the Company, the hunters were to be paid the following rates:

Elephants with tusks

For an animal 6 cubits high and upwards, a gold bracelet of 7 pagodas and rds. 40 in cash.
For an animal 5 to 6 cubits high, a gold bracelet of 6 pagodas and rds. 30 in cash.
For an animal 4 to 5 cubits high, a gold bracelet of 4 pagodas and rds. 20 in cash.
For an animal 3 to 4 cubits high, a silver bracelet of rds. 2 and rds. 12 in cash.

Alias [Aliyas] and female elephants without tusks

For an animal 6 cubits high and upwards, a silver bracelet of rds.2 and rds. 20 in cash.
For an animal from 5 to 6 cubits high, a silver bracelet as above and 15 rds. in cash.
For an animal of 4 to 5 cubits, rds. 10 and no bracelet.
For an animal 3 to 4 cubits, rds. 6 and no bracelet.[124]

† A pagoda was a gold coin and one cubit is an ancient measure of length derived from the forearm, usually about 45–50cms

Death at Panamure – The Last Kraal

The last kraal in Sri Lanka was held in August 1950 at Panamure in the Southern Province. It was organised by Sir Francis Molamure, Speaker of the Parliament, and Mr Sam Elapata Senior, Disawe (Governor) of Atakalan Korale in Ratnapura district.[125] Sir Francis supervised the building of the stockade as well as the subsequent elephant drive. Many hundreds of local villagers rallied to help in the process and dozens of dignitaries journeyed from around the world to observe the event.

Eighteen elephants were driven into the vast stockade that had taken more than three months to build. Fifteen of those trapped were later identified as suffering with gunshot wounds. The kraal was clearly not their first encounter with man. But for one large bull elephant, the Panamure kraal became a tragic and defiant final encounter. The bull displayed an extraordinary and relentless resistance. He was quickly identified as a threat to the entire operation. He charged anyone who dared venture near him. His concern was clearly not just for himself. With colossal strength he sustained a fierce and fearless battering of the barricades in a vain struggle to set the herd free. Assuming that the elephant would soon tire, the organisers postponed the entry of the tame elephants. But the bull continued his rage, pausing only to carry food to his fellow captives. Finally the tame elephants were ordered into the stockade. With unparalleled ferocity the raging bull immediately knocked the lead tame elephant to the ground. Ideas of releasing the bull were quickly dismissed. An elephant in such a state would cause untold destruction to anything in its path. Eventually Sir Francis Molamure issued the order. The bull elephant was to be destroyed. The massive creature resisted to the last. Witnesses claim that he met his death *charging and trumpeting defiance.*[126]

News of the shooting triggered a public outrage. Newspapers were flooded with letters of protest claiming that the kraals must stop if the elephants are to be given any chance of survival. *The Times* editorial stated that the spirit of the dead elephant *called for mercy and the right [of the elephant] to roam the wilds, a free citizen of Lanka.*[127]

In his death the wild bull became a national hero. Having fought not merely for his own rights but for those of his kin he had paid the ultimate price. Songs and stories were written about him, many of them apocryphal. They tell of his endless courage and are often recalled in tones of hushed amazement.

Death of the Parliamentary Speaker

There is widespread belief in Sri Lanka that whoever is responsible for the death of a tusked elephant will not live long. It is not certain whether the 'Panamure bull' was a tusker. While some witnesses claim that the bull definitely was not, others insist that the raging animal used its tusks to gore a tame elephant.

What is certain however, is that on 25 January 1951, just five months after he had given the order to shoot the bull elephant, Sir Francis Molamure died suddenly in parliament. He was 67 years old. Many claim that his death was 'divine retribution' for having issued the order to shoot the elephant.

Mr Dahanayake, former Prime Minister of Sri Lanka, was a Member of Parliament at the time of Sir Francis' death. Speaking from his home in Galle, at the age of 90, he recalled the details vividly. 'Sir Francis rose slowly from his chair and then collapsed in a heap on the floor'. Others claim that the Speaker fell to his knees in a manner identical to the last moments of the Panamure bull. When asked if Sir Francis' death was somehow connected with the shooting of the elephant Mr Dahanayake replied 'Some may say that. I wouldn't'.

Executioners and Instruments of War

From the time elephants were first enslaved by men they suffered not only as beasts of burden but also as awesome weapons of destruction. It was probably through fear of the ankus that elephants were trained as executioners for the kings. A prisoner, summonsed to 'death by elephant' had his head placed on a block and crushed under the elephant's forefoot. In another method the unfortunate prisoner lay on the ground while the elephant ripped his limbs from his body.

Another means of execution required the prisoner to be roped between two flexible trees. The elephants would bend the trees inwards toward each other. Following a command they would then release their grip. As the trees sprang apart, the man was torn to death.

The engagement of Sri Lankan elephants in warfare is well chronicled and indeed, legendary. They were employed in local conflicts between the Sinhalese and Tamils and later against the colonial invaders. In the famous battle for Colombo of 1587, King Raja Sinha I is said to have gathered over 2,000 elephants against the Portuguese. Elephants were also shipped to distant lands to fight other people's wars.

To accustom these gentle giants to the noise and blood of war, wild animals were slaughtered in front of them. On the battlefield the elephants were plied with alcohol and goaded forward. They learnt to brandish heavy chains or sharp swords in their trunks as they slashed their way through enemy lines. Sometimes they would simply scoop up an enemy and thrust him to the ground, or pass him to the soldiers who would quickly finish him off.

The sheer sight of a phalanx of war elephants sent many an unprepared enemy scurrying in retreat. But when meeting a prepared army, the elephants suffered horrific wounds. Their protective leather coverings proved ineffective against the molten lead that rained down from city fortresses or from the poisoned arrows that pierced the trunk or gouged the eyes.

It was not uncommon in battle for an enemy foot soldier to sneak close to the elephant and hack its feet and trunk with a sharp axe. Wounded elephants that did not die in battle were likely to retreat and turn on the very men who coaxed them into such horror.

The employment of elephants in the front lines of battle was a practice destined to end. Fire, flaming spears and other atrocities often caused the elephants to panic. Panicking elephants led to an army in disarray and confusion. Improved technologies of war, combined with the fact that elephants are notoriously fussy eaters, expensive to transport and reluctant to fight, hastened their demise as instruments of destruction.[128]

Entertainers and Performers

While elephants were in demand for work, they were also employed for sport and performance. During the time of the early kings, elephant fights would be staged as popular entertainment. To this day elephant performances continue. Elephant races are popular as a feature of special celebrations such as New Year festivities. And each day hundreds of people flock to see elephants perform in the arena at the Colombo Zoo.

The Colombo Zoo

It happens every day at 5.15 p.m. In an amphitheatre not far from where the lions pace dementedly in their small cages, the elephants strut their tricks before throngs of locals and tourists.

It is indeed a remarkable sight to see elephants standing on their heads and kicking their hind legs in the air; playing the harmonica; skipping to the beat of a drum and walking backwards into line to wait patiently before being called for the next trick. But should we applaud the domination of one species by another?

There are those who say that because the elephant can be trained to perform such extraordinary acts, its intelligence must be questioned. But how often have humans (supposedly the most intelligent species on earth) imprisoned fellow humans and conditioned them into performing extraordinary acts?

There's no doubt that these zoo elephants are well looked after. Their colour and demeanour reveal a benevolent environment. But what dignity is there in having to dance for your supper?

Hunting for Sport and 'Vermin'

The slaughter of elephants accelerated dramatically during the colonial period, especially under the British. In the 1840s and 1850s, rewards were paid for the destruction of nearly 6,000 elephants. This is more elephants than currently exists on the entire island. Such genocide was justified by the perception of elephants as 'vermin' and a threat to life and property.

By the mid 19th century, elephants with tusks were already a rarity. In 1855, the explorer and hunter, Sir Samuel Baker wrote:

> *...a tusker is a kind of spectre, to be talked of by a few who have had the good luck to see one. And when he is seen by a good sportsman, it is an evil hour for him – he is followed till he gives up his tusks.*[129]

So intense was the hunting that the government reward of 'ten shillings per tail' was reduced and even abolished in some districts because of the high annual outlay. Aside from government money, the main reward to a sportsman for killing an elephant was a massaged ego. If the elephant was a tusker, the ivory would be immediately removed and sold. Some shooters would hack off the elephant's feet or perhaps even its leg to the knee. These dismembered pieces became ashtrays or umbrella stands in the rooms of a 'gentleman's residence'. Sometimes the pieces of the elephant were kept merely as trophies. However, in most cases, the elephant carcass would be left to rot where it fell.

The Elephant Hunt as illustrated by the Prussian Prince Waldemar (1844 –1846).

He accompanied Major Thomas Rogers on hunting expeditions.

Legends of Elephant Shooters

Death of Major Rogers

During his period as District Judge and Assistant Government Agent (1834–1845) in the British Colonial regime, Major Thomas William Rogers achieved a reputation for gallantry. He was particularly renowned for his horsemanship and his jungle skills. He was also a keen sportsman. He shot and killed over 1,400 elephants.

Many times Rogers courted death. On one occasion he was coaxing his horse across a swollen river. A floating log caused the horse to panic. Despite almost superhuman efforts Rogers could not save his fine Australian steed. Drenched and dispirited, he began the long walk home when he heard a familiar but threatening sound. He was in the path of a wild and charging elephant.

Rogers scrambled frantically into the bow of a tree. The raging elephant grabbed Rogers' leg and then screamed with pain as the spur from the Major's riding boot pierced his sensitive trunk. Eventually the boot fell to the ground. The enraged beast stamped and tore at the boot until it was completely destroyed. Then grasping the remains in his trunk, he hurled them high into the air, to another part of the forest.

Rogers' final encounter was not with an elephant but with an even more powerful force of nature – lightning. On the morning of 7 June 1845, the Major was at the Haputale rest house in the hill country with some colleagues. A heavy rainstorm prevented the party from leaving on schedule. Rogers wandered to the verandah to check the weather. He noted that the rain had all but stopped and the sun was peering through the parting clouds. But suddenly a streak of lightning came 'from out of the blue' and struck Rogers on the spur of his riding boot. He collapsed and died immediately.

It is claimed that moments later, a member of Rogers' party heard an elephant trumpeting which *seemed to carry a strange, vibrant note of savage triumph.*[130]

Major Rogers was buried in Nuwara Eliya, in the hills in central Sri Lanka. A deep crack divides his neglected gravestone. Some say lighting has shattered his grave.

There are many who claim that the death of Rogers was divine retribution for killing so many elephants, especially tuskers. The fact that it was Rogers' spur that had harmed the wild animal and that it was his spur that was struck by lightning adds mystery and intrigue to the event. But the intrigue deepens. Mythology links elephants with rain. And Rogers was killed by that harbinger of rain – lightning!

Others claim that the Major's gallantry as a sportsman saved many lives. Elephants had become a regular threat to the villagers. By killing so many, Rogers had reduced the threat.[131]

Disturbing Ireson's Grave

On a rocky hill at the tiny settlement of Sella Kataragama, not far from the shrines and temples of the Kataragama township, stands a pinnacled marker to the final resting place of English sportsman, Mr J.P. Ireson, who died in 1923, aged 66. The grave was erected by his friends the following year.

Over the decades the grave has been disturbed many times. On each occasion it was repaired but the destruction continued. Once the entire pinnacle was toppled. It was re-erected with a protective iron railing cemented around the perimeter. That railing has since been severely bent. Some people claim that it is the wild elephants in the surrounding jungles that cause the damage. They say that because Ireson bagged many elephants with his sportsman's gun, the elephants will not leave him alone. Others dismiss such phenomena. Whatever the truth, it seems that Ireson has definitely not been allowed to rest in peace.

A Continuing Dilemma

As more land was devoted to plantations so the struggle between farmers and elephants intensified.

The dilemma confronting many plantation owners was well illustrated by the predicament facing Mr Aloy Jayakody in the early 1960s. His 16 hectare estate became a favourite ground for a herd of elephants which threatened to destroy the property. Permission to capture the elephants was refused but, at that time, shooting in defence of crops was allowed.

> *In one year Mr Jayakody and his staff shot and burnt 23 elephants. The burning carcass of the 23rd elephant burst open to reveal a fully formed baby. Mr Jayakody was so distressed that he made up his mind that there would be no further shooting without another strenuous effort to obtain a permit to capture.*[132]

One person who shot many elephants, albeit only with a camera, was the renowned Sri Lankan wildlife photographer Eric Swan. However, Swan's luck expired when, in September 1951 a large elephant, near Polonnaruwa turned suddenly and charged. The elephant crushed him with her massive forefeet before disappearing into the jungle. Swan died within hours.

News spread that family and friends planned to hunt and kill the elephant. The *Daily News* published letters of protest about the proposed hunt. One letter from the Minister of Justice, Dr L. A. Rajapakse, stated:

> *...I appreciate very much the acceptance of my suggestion that Mr Swan's brother and friends should give up the proposal to track down and kill the she elephant. After all, the trespass was on her jungle domain of which she was a monarch, and she must have been frightened at the sight of men with cameras. I trust no others will undertake to hunt this elephant.*

A letter from William A. Blake, who was with Swan when he was killed, stated:

> *...Of all the animals of the jungle there is none I have had greater respect for than the elephant. The accident ...was due to no fault of the elephant but our own. Encouraged by earlier successful encounters with elephants we moved in too close and paid the penalty with a life...*

Blake reassured all that he had no intention of hunting the elephant and he appealed to all hunters to leave the elephant to heal its wounds in peace.[133]

Shooting elephants, even in the defence of crops, is now outlawed. But despairing farmers and villagers sometimes take the law into their own hands. They use guns, steel traps or poisoned water to deter the elephants.

Above: The inscription on the gravestone of Major Rogers reads:
IN MEMORY OF MAJOR THOMAS WILLIAM ROGERS OF HER MAJESTY'S CEYLON RIFLE REGIMENT MANY YEARS COMMANDANT AND ASSISTANT GOVERNMENT AGENT AT BADULLA.
STRICKEN TO DEATH BY LIGHTNING...ON THE 7TH OF JUNE 1845 AGED 41 YEARS.
Some claim that the death of Major Rogers was 'intervention of the gods' for having killed over 1,400 elephants. They further claim that lightning still strikes his grave.

Above: Mr Dahanayake, former Prime Minister of Sri Lanka, was in the parliament when the Parliamentary Speaker, Sir Francis Molamure, collapsed and died in January 1951. Many believe that Sir Francis' death was divine retribution for having issued the order to shoot an elephant. Mr Dahanayake comments, 'Some may say that. I wouldn't.'

Right: This pinnacle marks the final resting place of English sportsman Mr J.P. Ireson who died in 1923 aged 66. It has been disturbed many times. Once the entire pinnacle was toppled. Local villagers claim that because Ireson killed so many elephants, the wild elephants will not let him rest in peace.

ELEPHANTS AT WORK

ELEPHANTS have been instrumental in the construction of both ancient and modern Sri Lanka. They levelled the site of the first *Thupa* (domed edifice housing a Relic Chamber). During the reign of the kings, they removed tonnes of soil for the sophisticated tanks and irrigation systems. Such systems were essential to the livelihood and wellbeing of the people and many of them are still in use today. They also carried the soil from which millions of mud bricks were made for construction in the ancient cities.

As the island economy opened to world trade, elephants cleared the way for tea, coffee and rubber plantations. They hauled logs from the forests and carried heavy materials for construction of new buildings. They played a vital role in the building of roads and railways. In fact many of the roads which elephants helped to construct were engineered to follow the traditional elephant routes. These were widely recognised as simply the most appropriate pathway.

> *...the sagacity which they display in 'laying out roads' is almost incredible...[government surveyors observed] that in crossing the valleys from ridge to ridge, through forests so dense as to altogether obstruct a distant view, the elephants invariably select the line of march which communicates most judiciously with the opposite point...*[134]

Even in more modern times elephants have been engaged on some significant construction projects. In 1992, they helped position the massive pillars used in the new shrine hall at the Sacred Tooth Temple in Kandy.

Carrying Capacity

Temple paintings show elephants harnessed to ploughs and even carriages. Sometimes they carried loads on their backs. However, most work undertaken by elephants in Sri Lanka consists of carrying and manipulating loads with their trunks, tusks, foreheads and feet.

A healthy adult elephant can carry about 500 kilos on its back. With careful co-ordination of its trunk, legs and entire body mass it can shift and re-position weights of up to four tonnes.

But it is a mistake to think of an elephant as an insensitive beast capable of unbounded feats of strength and endurance. They are highly sensitive creatures that need adequate food, water and rest. They also need understanding and tenderness. They should not be worked if they are too young (below 15) or too old (over 50), if they are pregnant or recovering from an illness, if the weather is unduly hot or the weight is excessive.

Riding an Elephant to Death

For overworked elephants, the repercussions can be traumatic as revealed by Sir Samuel Baker. Prior to his famous expedition to the Upper Nile, the 19th century explorer spent eight years in Ceylon (1847 – 1855). To look after his horses, Baker employed a groom named Henry Perkes.

Perkes was a heavy drinker and very accident prone. His negligence once caused a team of horses complete with carriage and supplies to fall over a cliff. The horses had to be destroyed. Baker was determined to salvage what he could. He sent Perkes with an elephant and mahout to assist in *'hauling the fallen carriage up the precipice'*. Perkes chose to ride the elephant rather than walk alongside it. And he insisted the mahout work the elephant into a trot. The mahout protested that such a pace would injure the elephant. Perks issued threats to the mahout and so, according to Baker:

> *...the beast was soon swinging along at full trot forced on by the sharp driving hook with the delighted Perkes striding across its neck riding an imaginary race.*[135]

The following day Baker was met by the elephant driver without the elephant. Perkes had forced the elephant at an intolerable pace up a steep pass for 12 kilometres. The elephant collapsed and died. Baker was not impressed.

> *Mr Perkes was becoming an expensive man: a most sagacious and tractable elephant was now added to his list of victims; and he had the satisfaction of knowing that he was one of the few men in the world who had ridden an elephant to death.*[136]

Route between Colombo and Kandy as illustrated by the Russian Prince Soltykoff (1841).

Machines are now more economical than elephants. But there are still an estimated 500 working elephants in Sri Lanka. They labour mostly in the timber industry, dragging logs and loading trucks. Sometimes they work as gardeners clearing small patches of land.

Today in Sri Lanka it is customary for working elephants to rest in the afternoon when the sun is at its fiercest.

A new demand for elephant labour has developed with an expanding tourist and travel industry. Some elephants are engaged to carry camera-toting tourists into the jungles to photograph what little wildlife may be left. Others may be used to greet dignitaries at airports and hotels. For some people the presence of a lone elephant dressed in all its regalia standing for hours in the heat amidst the traffic fumes offers a sense of occasion. For others it is a pitiable reminder of the extent to which the dignity of these wondrous creatures has diminished.

Elephants have been instrumental in the construction of both ancient and modern Sri Lanka. They levelled the site for the first Thupa, they removed tonnes of soil for the sophisticated irrigation systems and, during the colonial period, they cleared land for plantations. Though machines are replacing elephants, approximately 500 working elephants exist in Sri Lanka today. To watch an elephant load logs is to witness a unique combination of skill, strength and ability for symmetry, precision and balance.

Menika Loads Some Logs

Menika stood firm with her hind legs slightly apart and her front legs bent at the knees. Her long thick trunk was curled inwards. The dome of her head rested neatly against the end of the massive log that seemed precariously balanced on the archaic and rickety truck. For a moment she closed her eyes tight. Very slowly she pushed against the log with her full body weight. As if on casters, the heavy log glided smoothly into position.

Menika released her weight and took a couple of steps back. Quietly she surveyed her handiwork. Seemingly satisfied with what she had accomplished she turned around, bent low and placed her trunk firmly around the end of the next log on the ground. She lifted the end, pulled it toward the truck and balanced it on the edge of the space that she had created. She then walked backwards to the other end of the log that was still on the ground, lifted it and pushed it into position. Once again she employed her forehead and full body weight to make the final adjustments.

The whole scene was remarkably silent save for the sporadic clang of the bell around Menika's neck or the occasional command from the young mahout who sat lazily astride her neck enjoying the breeze generated by her flapping ears. At times the mahout would move his bare feet behind her ears to direct her, but for the most part, Menika worked without instruction.

When a heavy vehicle careened down the narrow road belching offensive smoke, sounding horn and screeching brakes, Menika took no notice. A disciplined elephant, she is able to remain focussed on the task at hand.

Since early morning Menika had been loading and balancing logs. After midday she would head to the river to escape the heat, have some lunch and relax. Unless an evening job became available, Menika would not work again until the following morning.

Like many working elephants in Sri Lanka, Menika was captured from the jungle when she was very young. Her training began immediately. Now, aged about 30, she has 15 years of working experience behind her. Assuming she lives to enjoy old age, she can look forward to another 15 years work before her strength diminishes and she retires.

Baby Nona – A Retired Worker

After 30 years pulling timber from the jungles, Baby Nona (Little Lady) is now retired. Today the 50 year-old elephant lives a quiet and sedate life on the 12 hectare estate of businessman, Mr Jayantha De Silva. Whenever the opportunity arises, Sunil, her mahout takes Baby Nona to a temple procession. 'It gives her the chance to be with other elephants' says Mr De Silva. Although she no longer works, Baby responds to Sunil's commands to pick up logs and transport them from one part of the garden to another. The exercise maintains her strength.

Baby Nona has known periods of illness but after intensive veterinary treatment she has regained her health. Now she looks happy and content. 'She thinks this land belongs to her' says Jayantha De Silva. 'If someone takes some leaves she will cry and trumpet. Nobody is allowed to pluck anything from these trees'.

Elephants have been in the De Silva family for several generations. Baby Nona is the last in line. 'We probably won't replace her when she goes. It's very expensive to keep an elephant these days. There isn't that much work for them so they cannot earn their keep. And we find that we have to go further and further away to bring in food for her'.

Sometimes, when it is dark and the household is asleep, Baby Nona cries and trumpets until someone comes to her. They say she has nightmares. Rubbing her trunk they comfort her, 'Don't worry Baby Nona, we're here'. 'Every day we talk to her' says Mr De Silva. 'She's just like another member of our family. We can't imagine what it will be like when she's gone'.

Like many elephant owners, the De Silvas believe that elephants bring good luck. 'As long as there is an elephant, everything will be provided'.

Below: At the Veterinary Department of the Peradeniya University near Kandy, mahouts bring their sick elephants to be examined and treated by Dr Kuruwita and Dr De Silva.

Above: After 30 years of work, Baby Nona, aged 50, is now retired. She lives with her owners, the De Silva family. To maintain her strength she occasionally carries logs. Like many who respect the elephant, the De Silvas believe that 'As long as there is an elephant, everything will be provided'.

MEDICINES AND THE WORKER

*W*HEN treating sick domestic elephants, veterinarians employ the full range of modern medicines, including antibiotics and vitamins. There are still some doctors who prefer the more traditional treatments involving complex combinations of particular plants and seeds. Such treatments are becoming increasingly difficult to procure as it is necessary to travel further and further into the jungles to collect the ingredients.

Traditional Cures

Traditional Sinhalese elephant cures exist for a wide range of ailments from digestive troubles and sore feet to skin disease, diabetes and cancer. Some of the remedies involve complex concoctions that would take many hours, if not days, to prepare. A traditional remedy for cancer, for example, requires 23 ingredients to be ground with the latex from certain trees in a small earthen container. The instructions are to:

> *...Keep the vessel containing the mixture under a stack of paddy for a good number of days and apply some on the affected part in the form of a plaster on a piece of cloth...*[137]

Some cures entail a pill, about the size of an orange, made from mixing specific measures of 25 ingredients. The instructions are to:

> *Make of this mixture pills of the size of Bulu (Terminalia bellerica) fruits and dry them in the shade...[The pills are administered] for loss of appetite, sun bathing and swallowing of soil. Give three desiccated coconuts (Kotta pol) with three pills for three days. Give pills for same in oranges, or mixed with boiled Panudiya (rice water). For all types of diseases give the pills inserted in lime fruits or with gingeley (sesamum) oil cake.*

> *Bury a pill in the elephant stall or have one in the sash round the elephant's neck to ward off disease.*[138]

Elephant Wilbert's skills in the traditional cures for elephant ailments are highly respected in Sri Lanka. 'I read the elephant like an astrologer reads the palm of the hand. We must listen to the elephants'.

Rendezvous with Raja
Attending a Sick Elephant

The white van that met us at our hotel was driven by Mr Hemantha Piyasiri, a young Colombo businessman and owner of a sick elephant called Raja. Our first stop was to collect Dr Kodikara from his veterinary practice in a northern suburb of Colombo.

In the tradition of urban veterinary surgeons, much of Dr Kodikara's work concerns dogs, cats and other pets of the wealthy classes. But elephants are his true passion. His thorough documentations detail his work with numerous elephants over many years.

Forty minutes later we arrived at the home of Mr Siripala, Raja's mahout for 40 years. In Mr Siripala's absence, 19 year-old Saman was in charge. Grabbing his ankus, Saman mounted his pushbike and rode along the dirt track to a nearby lake where Raja was relaxing. We followed in the vehicle.

From a distance the shape in the water looked like a massive shiny black boulder. In fact it was Raja. He lay completely still on one side. Apart from his bulk, only the end of his trunk, part of his large domed head and an eye were visible. Gentle ripples danced across the lake from the breath that he expelled. In the heat of the day his breath was slow and irregular. Aside from the ripples, there was no movement. Dark clouds hung low and close. There was a suffocating stillness. Raja was asleep.

Saman gripped the ankus with one hand and hitched his sarong with the other. Without hesitating he waded through the water toward Raja. 'Daha' he yelled. The sharpness of his voice defied his gentle manner. Slowly Raja opened his eye. 'Daha' Saman yelled again, even sharper this time. Raja began to sway his massive body building up the momentum required to stand. 'Daha' came the order again.

As Raja heaved himself awkwardly into a standing position, the ripples became small waves that slapped against the muddy banks. Saman barked some further commands and Raja gathered the heavy chains attached to his leg. With one swing of his trunk he tossed the chains across his neck. He walked out of the lake toward the open grassy space. There he would be examined and given drugs.

At 55 Raja looked older than his years. The usual richness of colour had turned pale and insipid. His once powerful forelegs seemed to sag under the burden of his own weight. His walk was more of a defeated shuffle than the sprightly gait of a healthy elephant. His head remained low.

Raja became part of the Piyasiri family 25 years ago at the request of a Buddhist priest. Concerned about the diminishing elephant population and disappearing traditions, the priest proposed that Mr Piyasiri Senior maintain an elephant. Mr Piyasiri agreed. Such generosity keeps elephants healthy and ancient traditions alive. As well as Raja, Hemantha Piyasiri owns Kumari who, in 1989, gave birth to a male called Jayithu.

In the 25 years that Raja has been part of the Piyasiri family, he has had very few days of sickness but in recent months he has shown signs of chronic fatigue and diminished appetite. Mr Piyasiri has spent much effort to diagnose and cure Raja's illness.

Saman commanded Raja to lie on the grass. 'Hida' he yelled several times as Raja bent his rear legs and then his front legs. Slowly he lay to one side and curled his trunk over his face. For the next 90 minutes Dr Kodikara and a team of local helpers went about their business. A small crowd of villagers gathered to watch.

Raja was suffering lethargy and loss of appetite. Dr Kodikara discusses Raja's treatment with Mr Piyasiri, owner and Saman Siripala, mahout.

It took a long time to break off the tops of dozens of tiny bottles containing antibiotics and vitamin B12 and to draw their contents into the large syringe. Antiseptic cream was applied to Raja's backside before the needle was plunged through his sensitive skin into a vein. Raja barely flinched. But he did keep his eyes closed and his breathing seemed even slower and heavier.

There were four needles altogether. The final one bent on the way in but Raja lay quiet and still, as if he knew that all the attention was for his benefit.

Dr Kodikara receives assistance from local villagers in the preparation of Raja's treatment – vitamin B12 and antibiotics.

At one stage during the treatment Raja defecated. His first droppings were slow and doubtless painful. But later droppings were easier. On examining the output Dr Kodikara was optimistic.

With the injections finished, Saman commanded Raja to stand. He then walked the elephant across the paddock, giving Dr Kodikara a chance to observe his gait. Raja looked even more tired than when he first emerged from the water. But Dr Kodikara observed improvements.

Several months later Raja had regained much of his strength and was well on the way to a full recovery.

On completion of his treatment, Raja stands up for a final inspection.

THE ELEPHANT KEEPERS
MAHOUTS

*M*AHOUTS tend to be aloof. Their lean, lithe and weathered bodies are often clad in minimal but colourful sarong. Some sport faded tattoos on their leathery skin. Some wear gold medallions or bracelets of elephant hair. Their sharp searching eyes, almost always fixed upon the elephants in their charge, reveal few secrets. They often stare but rarely engage.

The craft of the mahout is inherited. It has been passed from father to son for thousands of years.

However, today some mahouts are the first in their families to work with elephants and acquire a knowledge of elephant lore. Some have been inspired by a fascination and respect for the elephant. Others have drifted toward the life for want of anything else to do or because they happened to be a servant in the household of an elephant owner. These new mahouts acquire their skills by working as assistants to those more experienced.

Wherever there is a domestic elephant, there is a mahout. He might be walking his elephant from village to village in search of work to earn his keep. He might be at the river scrubbing his elephant vigorously with a coconut husk. In the heat of the day he may be stretched out, sleeping near his resting elephant, or perhaps even across the back of the elephant as it too lies down. At festival time he will walk his elephant many kilometres through the night to participate in the special pageants.

During the time of the kings, the knowledge and skills of the elephant keepers were widely valued. In the rigid and hierarchical caste system, they held a position second only to farmers and equal to that of skilled artisans who worked with gold and silver. Beneath them came the potters, clothes washers, weavers and soldiers. The class of the elephant men was permitted seats and the wearing of doublets.[139] Indeed, none beneath them attained such privilege.

The Knowledge of the Mahout

The mahout's knowledge covers three main categories: caste, control and elephant wellbeing.

Caste

Sri Lankan mahouts who practice the ancient methods, insist that a deep understanding and appreciation of the elephant caste system is crucial to the elephant/mahout relationship. The elephant's caste will determine its behaviour and disposition. These characteristics further determine the methods adopted for handling and control. Some mahouts believe that early and accurate identification of caste is essential and that failure to comprehend and apply the principles leads to problems with elephants.

Through his understanding of the elephant caste, the mahout determines the life-span, courage, suitability for training, temperament, fads with food and auspiciousness of an elephant. For example, by identifying an elephant in the Mangala caste, the mahout would acknowledge its arrogance and be assured that it is harmless.

Attributes of a Good Mahout

A mahout should be:

† Of moderate size
† Good tempered
† Sober
† Educated

His knowledge should include:

† Elephant lore
† The nila (points for goading the elephant)

He must be proficient with:

† *The Silinguva* (a structure, restricting an elephant whilst it receives treatment)
† *The Thiringeye* (a pole used with a tourniquet for controlling elephants)

He should also possess the following articles of his profession:

† *Helle* (spear with a three centimetre head)
† *Ankus* (goad)
† Two bells
† *Kare-kambe* (neckrope of kitul fibre)
† *Porodde* (plaited rope with brass or copper hooks)
† Deer skin noose
† Wide bamboo leaf hat
† Large knife
† Iron chain[140]

Control

Apply upon the ankus a preparation made by grinding Kumburu seeds with cow's urine, and hook the spot six centimetres below the eye, the elephant will be subdued.[141]

The mahout employs a number of methods to achieve control of the elephant. He may use the ankus, his unique language, charms, and prayers. But beyond all this, it is the nature of the relationship between the elephant and the mahout that ultimately determines control.

Ankus: The ankus is a traditional stick, about two metres long with a point and hook at one end. The elephant has sensitive points throughout its body called *nila*. By prodding the *nila* or nerve centres with the ankus, the mahout causes the elephant to perform a wide range of movements and functions. The depth of the prodding is dependent on the animal's caste. With expertise the mahout prods the appropriate *nila*, to cause the elephant to raise its head, lie down, kneel, become subdued or obedient.

Language: *'Daha'* shouts the mahout. The elephant moves forward. *'Hida'*, and the elephant lies down. With about 30 words the mahout directs the elephant to assume various positions or to perform numerous tasks. These words, almost as ancient as elephants themselves, are often used in conjunction with physical contact. However, where a strong rapport exists between the mahout and the elephant, it is possible to exert control with minimal or even no contact. A gentle tap on the leg, or a slight touch of the ears and the elephant will respond. At times the relationship is such that the mahout merely thinks and the elephant will act appropriately.

Whilst riding the elephant the mahout uses his feet, positioned at the back of the elephant's ears to direct it. A gentle nudge with either leg will steer the elephant in the appropriate direction. Other body movements convey different messages such as stop or kneel.

Charms and Mantras: Charms are still used amongst those who follow the traditional ways of caring for and relating to elephants. A charm is simply an incantation or a mantra that may be issued either directly in the presence of an elephant or indirectly upon instruments used in the handling of elephants. The charms are most often used to quell the charge of a wild elephant. They have also been used in the taming of captive elephants and the healing of sick elephants.

Whilst some people cynically claim that the slamming of a car door or even a loud cough will have more effect on a charging elephant than a charm, others remain convinced that charms do work.

Elephant Language

Daha .... Go forward
Hida .... Lie down
Hari .... Get hold of
Pic cit .... Let go
Bila .... Raise leg for mahout
               to mount
Bilama puru ...... Push object forward
               with forefoot
Deri .... Eat or drink
Ida .... Give way
Pimbu .... Trumpet
Purur .... Push or attack
Dana .... Kneel
Udu deri .... Raise trunk[142]

Charms and Mantras

ACTION REQUIRED	ACTION TO BE TAKEN	MANTRA TO BE RECITED
Stop a charging elephant		*Om Kasalli Jata mata pita jaho puna lila dapane hitu...*
Elephants to flee	Charm three lumps of termite hill clay. Keep them on the shoulder when going about	*Om ariravel murikara sivane tari nil. Om sallita jata mata pita janaho...*
Elephants to flee	Charm the stones and throw them at the elephants. Charm the palms and clap	*Om sastimata gulija suputra sivasati ane tari* [143]

The Elephant and the Nila

The diagram and list below show the *nila*, nerve centres on the elephant. Mahouts are aware of these points and the results of their prodding with the ankus. Death to an elephant can result from prodding on the *nila* depicted on the diagram with a circled cross.

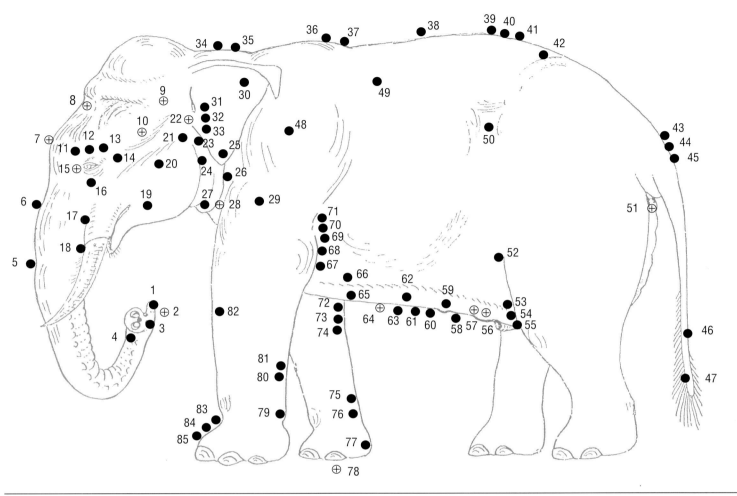

1	Twists trunk	**31**	Travels	**61**	Rouses, infuriates
2	Straightens trunk	**32**	Travels	**62**	Turns around
3	Frightens	**33**	Travels	**63**	Rouses, infuriates
4	Frightens and trumpets	**34**	Lowers head	**64**	Kills
5	Frightens, trumpets and stops	**35**	Benumbs	**65**	Stops
6	Brings under control	**36**	Stops animal as well as makes animal walk	**66**	Stops
7	Kills	**37**	Stops animal as well as makes animal walk	**67**	Stops
8	Kills	**38**	Lowers the seat	**68**	Stops
9	Kills	**39**	Frightens	**69**	Kneels
10	Kills	**40**	Frightens	**70**	Unknown
11	Brings under control	**41**	Frightens	**71**	Kneels
12	Brings under control	**42**	Unknown	**72**	Travels when two nilas are touched; Stops when one nila is touched
13	Rouses	**43**	Walks	**73**	As for 72
14	Brings under control	**44**	Walks	**74**	As for 72
15	Kills	**45**	Walks	**75**	Raises forefoot for mahout to mount
16	Kneels	**46**	Stops	**76**	Gives forefoot
17	Goes backwards	**47**	Travels	**77**	Raises forefoot for mahout to mount
18	Controls animal while being tied to a tree	**48**	Stops animal or makes it walk	**78**	Unknown
19	Gives shoulder	**49**	Offers seat	**79**	Lames and also brings hind foot forward
20	Lowers heel and neck and stops	**50**	Stays without fidgeting and puts trunk to ground	**80**	Offers hind foot and twists
21	Brings under control	**51**	Unknown	**81**	Offers hind foot and twists
22	Kills	**52**	Gets up and runs	**82**	Draws hind foot backward
23	Bends head	**53**	Turns around	**83**	Raises the forefoot
24	Stops	**54**	Turns around	**84**	Raises the forefoot
25	Rouses, infuriates	**55**	Turns around	**85**	Raises foot; mahout sets his foot upon middle toe nail of forefoot in mounting
26	Stops	**56**	Kills		
27	Offers seat	**57**	Kills		
28	Kills	**58**	Drops on the ground		
29	Stops	**59**	Turns around		
30	Brings under control	**60**	Rouses, infuriates	Diagram based on Dr P.E.P Deraniyagala's work.[144]	

Elephant Wellbeing

A good mahout is totally in tune with his elephant. He must be able to identify even the slightest signs of stress in the animal. He should be eternally vigilant in his examination of his elephant's skin, eyes, feet, tongue and even droppings. If he finds any irregularities such as an infection, a swollen muscle, a slovenly gait, too much undigested food or a weeping eye, he should understand the cause and know the remedies.

The Life of a Mahout

Today in Sri Lanka there is still status associated with owning an elephant. But the status of a mahout is ambiguous. For the life of a mahout is not an easy one. Pay is low and opportunities to supplement income by working the elephant are diminishing.

The daily routine of the mahout begins before sunrise and is rarely complete until well after sundown. He organises food and water for the elephant, conducts his customary inspection, bathes and scrubs his charge while diligently attending to any wounds or infections. He may also have to search for work. At the festivities, mahouts have the opportunity to meet others, to share stories and renew old acquaintances. But for the most, the mahout is alone with his elephant, and may spend more time with it than with his own family.

Between the elephant, the mahout and the elephant owner there exists a crucial symbiosis that can impact significantly on the wellbeing of the elephant. Some owners pay their mahouts an ample income thereby alleviating the need of the mahout to work the elephant hard in order to scratch a living. However, other owners expect the mahout to earn his keep primarily from the earnings of the elephant. This can lead to an overworked, tired and perhaps even aggressive elephant.

Mahouts vary considerably. Some can be cruel. They can harbour deep seated jealousies. Their fear of dismissal may lead to vengeful behaviour. The elephant world abounds with stories of mahouts, their sensitivity, their generosity, but also their cruelty.

In some cases mahouts have driven a small spike into a nerve on the back of the elephant's neck causing the elephant to endure constant pain when it is being ridden. This spike is virtually invisible. Except for the ruthless mahout who knows to avoid the spike, anyone attempting to mount the elephant, is likely to aggravate the pain and is therefore not welcomed by the elephant, who may become uncontrollable. The owner soon realises that only the one mahout is capable of controlling the elephant. By his action, an undetected mahout may ensure continued control over the elephant and preclude his own dismissal.[145]

Because of their arduous and often lonely lifestyle, some mahouts turn to alcohol.

A mahout had been working his elephant far from home. The job involved putting heavy fence posts into holes. With the work complete the mahout bathed his elephant, secured her to a tree and then became increasingly drunk from the local arrack. Eventually he passed out. The elephant broke free from her moorings, picked up the drunken man and placed him carefully on her back. Walking some kilometres through the night she arrived at the mahout's home. She lay him down gently at the doorstep, then stood waiting and watching, until his family woke and took care of him.

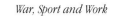

Top: These palm leaf manuscripts depict ancient elephant lore.

Centre: The sound of a bell heralds the presence of an elephant.

*Right: The tip and the hook of the ankus are used to goad the
elephant on special points known as nila.*

Other mahouts have not been so fortunate. Sometimes the reaction will be immediate; the elephant seizes the moment and fatally crushes the mahout. Other times the elephant may wait weeks, months and perhaps years before striking the mortal blow with trunk or leg. Having killed a mahout, an elephant is said to experience immediate remorse. It may cover the body with leaves and fodder. And it will often stand, moisture trickling from its eyes, guarding the corpse, forbidding anybody to approach.

> *An elephant...employed for more than 16 hours a day at a railway sleeper site at Kudapana suddenly turned on his mahout, killed him and threw his body into a nearby stream. It then ran amok...injuring ten other workers and damaging several village houses.*

> *Returning to the stream he removed the body of the dead mahout. For nearly six hours he stood there guarding the body. Then he disappeared into the jungles.*

> *Some believe the elephant had acted this way because of the long working day. In spite of several attempts to noose him, he was never recaptured.*[146]

However, it would be wrong to think of elephants as vengeful.

> *If the elephant habitually killed the man who punished him the mortality amongst mahouts would be very much more than it is now.*[147]

The genuine mahout is a paragon. Steeped in the ancient knowledge of his craft he exudes pride, wisdom and sincerity. He may be aloof. He may be warm and engaging. His relationship with the elephant flows naturally. He is confident in his art, and feels an honour, a privilege to be associated with a creature as sacred as the elephant. Such a mahout will announce with great humility: *Because the elephant is blessed with divine qualities, then to be in its presence, so too am I blessed.*

At the festivals, mahouts enjoy a break from the normal routine and a chance to enjoy the companionship of fellow mahouts.

Above: As keeper of the elephant, the mahout
spends many hours each day in attendance. His
unique knowledge and skills are inherited
through many generations.

Trimming the nails of an elephant and removing rough skin
minimises the potential for wounds and infections while
enhancing the growth of new, healthy tissue.

ELEPHANT OWNERS

*M*ythology links the elephant to the sacred, the divine. In ancient Sri Lanka elephants were associated with kings. Indeed only the kings owned elephants. Some kings reputedly owned thousands. They used them for war, for work and for ceremony. The *Gajanayake Nilame*, the custodian of the elephant stables enjoyed a high status ascribed to few.

After the rule of the kings, during the waves of colonial power, owning an elephant became a status symbol for established land holders as well as high ranking administrators. As the number of elephants on the island has declined, so too have the number of elephant owning families. Diminished work opportunities for elephants, shortage of appropriate food and clean water, smaller land holdings, difficulties in securing a good mahout and spiralling costs have contributed to this decline.

While there are some owners today who hope that they can sustain elephants in their families for generations, others know that the elephants they now have will almost certainly be their last. The status acquired through owning an elephant belongs to a different time.

Perhaps it is inevitable that the newly moneyed families of today seek to establish their status not with elephants but with other symbols such as cars and holiday homes in Europe. 'Elephants are too much trouble' said one wealthy businessman.

A sad outcome of the decline in elephant owning families, may be a decline in the knowledge about elephants. The custodians of such knowledge were the traditional owners. Through the generations they passed on the wisdom of elephant lore. They knew how to identify a good elephant and how to trap and tame a wild one without causing undue harm. They understood the herbal medicines. They lived a life that seemed more in harmony with the pace of these creatures. Above all, their wisdom and customs were intrinsic to the essence and survival of the culture.

Fortunately there are still people determined to sustain and share their knowledge. Some of them still own elephants, others can no longer afford them. As in the past, for current owners, 'Elephants are part of the family'.

Some owners visit their elephants every day. Others like their animals to be near their household. 'If my elephant is the first thing I see in the morning, I feel I'm going to have a good day' said one owner. 'I come to my elephant to meditate' said another. And for Mr Sam Elapata Junior, 'The elephant is the closest of all animals to God. That's why it stands for hours at a time and contemplates its previous births'.

Common to all those who know and care about elephants is a combination of hope and fear. The hope is that workable solutions to the complex problems of elephant versus human habitation can be found. The fear is that the elephant population of Sri Lanka will continue diminishing to the point where elephants may exist in memory and legend only.

Mrs Samarasinghe, with her elephant Puja, born in 1986. Sadly, during the writing of this book, Mrs Samarasinghe's husband, Mr Sam Samarasinghe, died in a tragic accident.

Mr Neranjan Wijeratne, Lay Custodian of the Temple of the Sacred Tooth Relic, with some of his elephants.

FIVE

CARING
FOR
ORPHANS

HAVE YOU BEEN TO PINNAWALA?

*H*AVE you been to Pinnawala? We were asked this question incessantly as we undertook our research. In fact it was Pinnawala that introduced us to the elephants. And it was Pinnawala to which we turned, and returned, as we progressed with our work.

Since it was established in 1975 with a handful of young elephants, the orphanage at Pinnawala has become a magnet that draws distressed baby elephants from around the island. Today the ten hectare site is near capacity with a population of 50 elephants.

Who knows what untold traumas the orphans at Pinnawala have witnessed? Denuded forests and diverted rivers have robbed elephants of their domain and have forced them into areas of human habitation. Sometimes a youngster will fall into a well or quarry. From there it may watch the frantic but hapless rescue attempts of its mother and aunts. The adults will not give up easily. But the safety and survival of the herd may force them to move on, trumpeting their grief as they leave the young one behind.

Sometimes a young elephant will be found standing beside the slaughtered carcass of its mother. The rest of the herd will have torn themselves away to escape the danger. But the young elephant will remain motionless, waiting as if the mere passage of time will return the life that once was.

A number of arrivals at the orphanage have borne the physical as well as emotional wounds of confrontation: a bullet lodged in a leg or eye; a festering foot wound from steel spikes. Unfortunately some elephants never arrive at the orphanage. Their injuries are so horrific, they do not survive. Elephants that tread on land mines in the war zone are so fated.

For the elephant that comes to the orphanage, the journey from its 'place of discovery' to its new home at Pinnawala will be as exhausting as it is disorientating. Having lost the comfort and security of its herd, where it frolicked with other youngsters, and suckled at will, it will be loaded onto a vehicle and transported to an environment of bottle milk, shelter sheds, human beings and restraining ropes.

Young elephants find companionship at the orphanage.

On arrival at the orphanage, the rescued baby is quarantined for a few days. Its state of health is assessed and a programme of recovery and re-adjustment is devised. When it joins the herd, the other elephants squeal as they rush to welcome the newcomer.

The new world for the young elephant may be small and contained. But it is a world where people are kind, food and water are abundant, medicines are administered and, most importantly, other elephants of all ages are on hand for support and lasting friendships.

Life for the elephants at Pinnawala parallels the life they would have enjoyed in the jungles. Their days consist of a seemingly endless cycle of eating, bathing and more eating. However, these elephants are under the continual command of the mahouts and the persistent gaze of bus loads of tourists. At night they are tethered.

For visitors to the orphanage the gates open at 8.30 a.m. But for the staff the day begins at dawn when the adult elephants are untethered.

Even before sunrise the babies are restless. Their formula milk is being prepared but it will still be a few hours before feeding begins. These elephants may be small but their trumpeting sends tremors through the ground. In the wild, to witness a young elephant feeding directly from its mother is to witness a picture of exquisite tranquillity. At the orphanage, to watch the babies feeding is to watch conspicuous and frenzied consumption. Each elephant raises its still undeveloped trunk as seven litres of formula milk are poured, one litre at a time, through a funnel directly into the mouth. Except for the rapid gulping action in their throats these babies remain totally still, their eyes fixed in an almost accusative gaze on the man with the milk.

However fast the staff work it is never fast enough. No sooner have the elephants finished gulping one litre they trumpet for the next. They work their tiny but already strong bodies into an almost frantic sway, with their eyes still fixed on the man with the milk. The babies seem to know when they have had their final bottle. Now their restlessness takes on a different form as they look beyond their feeding area to where the adult elephants are grazing.

After bottle feeding the babies are untied. In a tight bunch, some with milk still dripping from their mouths, they scurry toward the adults. The entire herd moves as one long, grey swaying creature through the entrance gates, across the road, past the souvenir shops and restaurants selling elephant statues and into the cool flowing waters of the Maha Oya river.

The river bathing, which lasts for two hours twice a day, follows a defined order. The mahouts command the larger elephants to lie down in the water. They form a straight row, each exposing one eye, one ear, a huge hump of carcass and maybe a leg. The tips of their trunks are just above the water. The odd ear flapping or swish of the tail is their only movement. With coconut husk in hand the mahouts clamber over them, scrubbing vigorously. Later they may stretch out along a lying elephant or squat within the shade of an overhanging rock. Wherever they are, the mahouts always have their ankus within reach and their sight firmly on their charges.

The rest of the herd wallow and play. Watching the elephants bathe is like watching a complex yet aesthetically orchestrated performance. They link and entwine trunks, spray water fountains, jump, pull tails, nuzzle up, race, spar and explore each other with intimacy, curiosity and delicacy. At times their contact seems reassuring. At other times they appear surprised as though meeting for the first time.

In the water the very young elephants usually remain flanked by the larger ones. Sometimes however, a small one will find itself apart from the group and it will stand very still in water up to its knees as it gazes toward the horizon. This herd of orphans requires constant reassurance. However far back their other life might be, that they will ever forget is unlikely.

At Pinnawala friendships can blossom into loving relationships. Sometimes the result is a newborn elephant. This has happened between Vijaya (*Victorious One*) and Kumari (*Princess*), two of the first orphans to arrive in the mid 1970s.

Kumari exudes serenity and a strong nurturing instinct. From the time she was young, the smaller elephants gravitated to her for security and contact. When her baby was born, she was already well experienced in the care of the young. On 5 July 1984, after a 22 month pregnancy, Kumari, still a teenager, gave birth to a daughter, Sukumari.

Above: Each day the Pinnawala orphans enjoy the waters of the Maha Oya Ganga.

Every day the baby elephants receive 21 litres of special formula milk over regular feeding sessions.

Today Sukumari is a strong, healthy and happy elephant. Her only knowledge of the dangers that confront her kind comes from her bonding with the newcomers. Like her mother, Sukumari captivates other young elephants. In 1989, when Sukumari was only five, Kumari had another baby to Vijaya. This one died soon after birth and it is said she grieved for three months. Her appetite diminished and she preferred solitude to company. Gradually she recovered. Four years later, Kumari gave birth to Esala.

Kumari is not the only female to have given birth at Pinnawala. A baby has also been born to Mathali in 1987, and to Komali and Anusha in 1989. In each case the father was Vijaya. He came to the orphanage in the mid 1970s. As a baby in the North Western province, he became separated from his herd. Vijaya has substance. His eyes flow with a tender protectiveness which is constantly expressed to the other elephants. His broad trunk bears the perfectly formed orange/pink markings of a high caste. His strong massive form moves with a majestic and flowing gentility that is befitting of the status ascribed to him. At Pinnawala it is Vijaya who is the appointed leader. He leads the herd on its twice daily journey to the river. On returning, no elephant may leave until Vijaya is standing. At the command of the mahout, his enormous profile, wet and glistening, rises out of the water. Moving forward onto the embankment, he waits just a few moments for the others to assemble behind. Then he moves off with 50 elephants in tow.

The elephants emerge from their afternoon session in the river to a final meal before sundown. For a short time each evening Nila, a large and gentle male, becomes a working elephant. Under minimal guidance he distributes the evening fodder that has been delivered by truck. Nila carries the large bundles of sweet, juicy kitul palm, jak fruit and tamarind to each elephant. He exercises his duty with great care and dignity, as if he knows that his work is contributing to the wellbeing of the other elephants.

At meal time the elephants are no longer one large interactive herd. Rather, they are individual entities totally absorbed by the task before them. The very young ones cannot control their trunks. Gripping small branches, they attempt to place these in their mouth, but they miss. Trunk and branch end up somewhere above the head. The struggle continues. Usually the food falls to the ground and the process begins again. Sometimes a small elephant will manage to place a log in its mouth. Balancing it with its trunk, it will attempt to chomp, but to no avail. The log is too thick. The little elephant has not yet learnt to strip the bark and smash the log with its feet, thereby reducing it to smaller pieces that it can readily lift to its mouth. Sometimes the small ones seem both fascinated and frustrated by their swinging proboscis which cannot yet accomplish the dexterous tasks performed by the grown-ups. They will continue to practice. And soon they will master the challenging co-ordination of trunk and forefeet.

Some of the elephants are tethered close together. Although each has its own bundle of fodder one may attempt to take the food of its neighbour. This activity is played out like a game; wait until your neighbour is momentarily distracted, perhaps taking food from its neighbour, and quickly stretch the trunk to grab what you can.

After the final feed it is time for rest. Most of the elephants are tethered for the night in large stables where they will sleep intermittently. The babies born in the orphanage are free to roam. They will not venture far from their mothers.

If, during the night the elephants lie down it will be for less than an hour. Long before sunrise they will begin to stir. Their bodies will sway and occasionally they will pierce the pre-dawn silence with a trumpet demanding their first feed for the day. Some will wait quietly and patiently. Others will be eager for the routine to begin, just as it did yesterday and just as it will tomorrow.

Bibile's Story

July 1991

He stands alone and apart. His yellow rounded body contrasts markedly with the tall thin black tree trunk. This is his only contact, a connection achieved via a rope. He appears listless and grumpy. His head hangs low, diminishing his one metre height. His trunk falls to the ground and curls. Except for an occasional grunt, he stands still and silent.

They call him Bibile, after the province where he was found. He is a month old, and this is his first week at the Pinnawala Elephant Orphanage.

A week ago he was probably enjoying the nurture and comfort of his mother's milk. His aunts would have fussed over him. Life would have been fun; suckling, darting between the huge column like legs of the adults, playing and bathing. But that life ended.

The villagers found him in a quarry, alone and deserted. Maybe in his mischief he wandered from the safety of his mother. No doubt his herd would have attempted a rescue. They may have spent days before realising the futility of their efforts. Perhaps they were forced to move on for their own survival.

At the orphanage, Mr Bandara, the Curator is quietly confident. Bibile will settle in.

But Bibile remains languid. He trundles to the river and reluctantly enters. He resists the stroking and nuzzling of the other elephants. Whilst babies shower and splash each other, he just hovers there in the water. With the bathing completed he trundles back, back to the thin black tree. His head hangs low, his trunk droops to the ground and recurls.

Ten Months Later

The thin black tree stands alone. In the distance baby elephants shriek as they receive their milk. Later they amble together to the river. Together they play. Where is Bibile? Now indistinguishable amongst the other elephants. In response to our question, Mr Sumanabanda wades out to the herd and returns with a black, rotund and spirited little elephant. 'This is Bibile'.

GIFTING OF ELEPHANTS

In one of his former lives, the Buddha was reincarnated as the King Vessantara. In a neighbouring province the people were suffering from the effects of drought. Poor harvests and inadequate water were creating malnutrition and disease. Concerned by this tragedy, King Vessantara gave to the people his white elephant, the bringer of rain, fertility and abundance.[148]

TO GIFT an elephant is to wish for the recipient all the qualities symbolised by the elephant: abundance, prosperity, strength and wellbeing. Sometimes an elephant from the Pinnawala orphanage is gifted to a temple or perhaps to another country. In 1991 Menika was presented to the people of Pakistan. A decade earlier Valli went to Wales, and earlier still in 1976, Shanthi went to the USA. On each occasion, the elephant has been accompanied by the curator or mahout to ensure that she settles into her new environment.

Valli's Story

It is a long way from the lush vegetation of Sri Lanka to the undulating hills of Wales. The climatic differences could hardly be greater. Yet these distant lands are linked by a strong sense of cultural identity, and by a Sri Lankan elephant named Valli.

In March 1980, when only a few weeks old, the tiny elephant was sighted by some villagers. She was grazing in the midst of a buffalo herd. The villagers became immediately worried. Without her mother's milk the elephant would surely die. A search for the mother revealed nothing and so the elephant was captured and transported to the orphanage at Pinnawala. At the orphanage Valli was quickly adopted by the adult elephants. She soon settled into the routine of eating, bathing and playing. She was called Valli, after the spouse of Skanda, one of the most popular deities in Sri Lanka.

However, Valli's destiny lay a long way from the orphanage in her native Sri Lanka. Thousands of kilometres away in Wales, near the village of Llanpumsaint, a group of dedicated people from many cultures and religions had formed a community called The Community of the Many Names of God. The community is based on the belief that there is only one philosophy of living underlying all the major faiths, that is *to serve all of God's creation*. People of every background and culture visit the community. In appreciation of support received from Sri Lankan visitors, the community donated 28 cattle to a Sri Lankan programme for the eradication of rural poverty. A grateful government of Sri Lanka reciprocated by donating little Valli.

Valli's Current Diet

Each day Valli consumes:

Breakfast

† Bananas

† Apricots

† ¾ kilo bran

† Two dessertspoons of salt

† Five grams of lime flour (for her bones)

Basic Diet

† Grass

In summer: 20 fertiliser bags per day

In winter: 45 kilos hay per day

Late Afternoon

† One kilo of rice – a special treat

Late Evening

† Barley Nuts: a mixture of barley, corn and molasses

During her Morning and Evening Walks

† Tidbits she finds, bramble, berries, bark

During the Day

† Copious quantities of water and tea When Brother Peter stops for his cup of tea, she too enjoys a litre of tea

Sweets

† Preference for peppermints

Valli arrived in Llanpumsaint in November 1981, only 18 months after she had been found in the Sri Lankan village.

As long as they can live peacefully, elephants can adapt to a wide range of environments. The cold, often harsh climate of Wales has not been a problem for Valli. A large heated stable has been built to make the winter months more comfortable. She has also enjoyed the constant companionship of Brother Peter, one of the community members. With help from Brother Henry, Brother Peter ensured that during her first two years in her new surrounds, young Valli received 24 hour attention. In fact, in much the same manner that adult elephants adopt baby orphans, the two brothers became Valli's adoptive parents. In one respect they had little choice. Whilst Brother Peter initially intended to sleep close by Valli, she had other ideas. Stretching out her trunk she pulled him closer to herself. Finally both Brother Peter and Brother Henry dossed down in the hay with her. She was content.

As a baby, Valli required special formula milk; cow's milk was not appropriate. With advice from the London Zoo, a local company was contracted to manufacture a special low-fat formula which would keep Valli healthy. Valli was about three years old when she was weaned off the milk. During her 15 months of bottle feeding at the Welsh community she had consumed a staggering 18,000 litres of formula milk. Now, as a young adult, Valli consumes vast quantities of local food produced especially for her. Brother Peter seeded a field with quick growing grass which he cuts frequently. This supplies the basic element in her diet.

Valli responds to a number of practical commands which enable Brother Peter to scrub her and inspect her feet, ears and skin for any injury or infection. Apart from Brother Peter, she lives with geese, ducks and dogs. On her daily walks, if she encounters a dog, she raises her back leg and 'gives a shriek of delight'.

She is a ceremonial rather than a working elephant. However, each year in December, she hauls a tree from the neighbouring forest into the grounds of the community. This is the Christmas tree.

Valli is well named, since the temple of the community is dedicated to the deity, Skanda. According to legend, this god, also known as Subramanya, was espoused to a young woman called Valli. When Valli the elephant participates in the Community's religious festivals, it is the image of the deity Skanda she will carry on her back.

It is not only the members of The Community of the Many Names of God who feel affection for Valli. The locals from surrounding villages call her 'our elephant'. She delights visitors to the temple and on occasions 'blesses' them by extending her trunk and touching their heads. She is believed to be the only elephant in Wales and for the people who have devoted their lives to the religious community she is much more than a good companion. She is a profound symbol of the very ideas and values that the community extols. In writing about the arrival of Valli to the Community, Brother Paul penned a version of the legendary tale about the blind men and the elephant.

> *The various limbs of the elephant that seemed separate and distinct to the blind seekers of its truth were all activated by the one stream of blood. Similarly, the various religions that feel separate and distinct are all fostered by a single stream of love.*

For the community, Valli, the Sri Lankan elephant, is a reminder of the truths and ideals to which they aspire.[149]

Patrick Horton

Far from Sri Lanka, in the Welsh village of Llampunsaint, Valli serves as an inspiration and source of enjoyment at The Community of the Many Names of God. Brother Peter ensures that she receives the companionship, nutrition and exercise that a healthy elephant requires.

Shanthi's Story

Cold blizzards and low temperatures have crippled Washington DC. It is covered in a thick stratum of ice. As a faint light pushes its way through the grey overhang, the treachery of the ice is apparent. Schools, businesses and even the White House are closed.

The zoo is also closed. It is encased in ice. Only the trees, fence palings and signs are visible. One sign bears the label 'Elephant House', but it points to a hollow where the snow and ice are much thicker than elsewhere. Maybe the blizzard has altered the direction of the sign. Yet down in the hollow a small entrance leads to a huge hangar-like building. In the centre of the hangar, tropical plants proliferate. And on the perimeter, small enclosures house rhinoceros, giraffes and elephants. There they stand, like models in shop windows, silent and peering out. In here the temperature is 30^0 C.

Black, tall and magnificent, almost completely filling her shop front, is Shanthi. Unlike the other animals she does not stand peering out. Her attention is diverted to the small pink newborn, sheltered between her legs. She watches, she strokes and she stands perfectly still when the little one, Kumari, begins to suckle. Other elephants in the next enclosure watch and extend their trunks. Shanthi grunts, removing Kumari from their presence. 'Shanthi is clearly jealous' remarks Marie Galloway, the head elephant keeper.

But who can know what memories may lie deep in Shanthi's being. When Shanthi was the age of her infant, she no doubt enjoyed the warmth and comforts of her herd. But one day in 1975 she fell into a well in a small Sri Lankan village. The villagers rescued her. She was taken to the orphanage at Pinnawala. But she did not stay there long. In 1976, when a year old, Shanthi was presented by the government of Sri Lanka to the people of the USA as a bicentenary gift.

At 18, Shanthi is a big elephant. She stands nearly three metres at her shoulder and she weighs 3,900 kilos. If anyone knows Shanthi, it is Marie Galloway. 'We understand each other' she insists. 'Our job as keepers is to be thinking one step ahead. But usually elephants are one step ahead of us. They know all our body movements and they really test the limits'.

At feeding time Shanthi stood very still and munched slowly on a bale of straw. Kumari used the opportunity to explore the possibilities of her dangling proboscis. At five weeks she could already collect pieces of straw with the end of her trunk and lift them toward her mouth. Actually placing the food in her mouth was still beyond her and she soon lost her grip. After several attempts she appeared to lose interest. Her eyes glazed over. Her movements become slower. She began to sway as if unbalanced. Then she toppled over and fell in the straw at her mother's feet. It was time for an afternoon nap.

Through Shanthi, the people of Sri Lanka have once again expressed the tradition of gifting elephants. Through Shanthi and Kumari the tradition lives on.

This large elephant Shanti was a bicentenary gift from Sri Lanka
to the people of America in 1976. In December 1993, at the
Washington Zoo, she gave birth to Kumari.

MR K.D. SUMANABANDA

EVERY evening, having satisfied himself that the orphaned elephants at Pinnawala are comfortable, content and securely tethered, Mr K.D. Sumanabanda mounts his sturdy bicycle and rides home to his village of Kotagama. The final half kilometre of his short journey takes him off the main road and across the elevated path that dissects the rice paddy. The world is different on the other side of the paddy. It is a world without cars, a world where natural sounds prevail and where people move at a different pace. Large rock slabs define the path to Sumanabanda's home, which squats on swept earth, surrounded by trees and vines. The windows and walls are adorned with elephant motifs. With pride and much laughter Sumanabanda claims 'This house was built by elephants'.

Mr Sumanabanda is distinguished amongst mahouts; the rice paddies he crosses are his own. His family, with links back to the Kandyan kings, has owned land and elephants for generations. They enjoyed a high caste status coming from the *Walawwa* class (a status similar to that of the Lord of the English Manor).

As the Chief Mahout at the Pinnawala Elephant Orphanage, Mr K.D. Sumanabanda assumes great responsibility. It is he who is in charge of Vijaya, the large splendidly marked male. It is he who supervises and organises the other mahouts, offering guidance in their dealings with the elephants. And it was he who accompanied Menika, the elephant donated to Pakistan, to ease her into her new environment.

Sumanabanda's vigilant eyes are directed constantly to his charges. If a baby elephant strays too far down stream, or a tourist ventures too close with a camera, Sumanabanda will notice. He can identify immediately each individual in the herd and he will eagerly talk on Kumari's pregnancies or the settling in of a new arrival.

Much like the creatures in his charge, Sumanabanda possesses both a strength and a gentility. His black curly hair frames his small face. His eyes, though small, are dark and prominent. His mouth readily parts into a broad smile. His body is lithe and slim. His athletic feet are equally at home on craggy mud, flat surfaces or steep uneven rocks. He moves with ease, ankus held high. In size he is small. But in stature he is elephant-like. In conversation his voice is strong but melodious and soft. Among the elephants this same voice may quietly cajole or issue a thunderous command to halt a mischief maker. Sumanabanda's agility, wisdom and humour combine to exude a warm and engaging essence. It is an essence that comes from devoting a lifetime to the elephants and, in return, allowing himself to be touched by them.

Sumanabanda has never been attacked by an elephant. In fact he is incredulous at such a notion. He explains that elephants are not creatures that attack or cause harm. He knows their caste, and respects their temperament. For him, life with elephants is part of the natural order.

When young, Sumanabanda listened very carefully to his father. By the time he was 12, he had mastered much of the unique language of the mahouts. He never missed an opportunity to be with elephants. As a young man he found employment at the Colombo Zoo. Through hard work and total dedication he was promoted to the Pinnawala Orphanage.

In his home Mr Sumanabanda is relaxed and somewhat coy. He has a strong sense of history, a sense of belonging to a time honoured tradition. His house is crammed with the traditional paraphernalia of the mahout, which he is proud and happy to display. Dressing himself in the ancestral garb of silk sarong with a belt of silver coins he stated, 'Mahouts took great care once; they dressed like this'. From a cabinet in his room he produced an ancient knife. Hundreds of years ago this knife tended an elephant's foot, perhaps one of the king's elephants. Sumanabanda then produced four sets of different sized hand cast brass bells. The music of these bells conjured immediate images of the rhythmic gait of colourfully dressed elephants, of rituals and of pageants. 'Elephants like the bells. They know they're going to the festival'.

The parade of past treasures continued for nearly two hours. Out came more bells, another knife, some old chains and an ancient ankus used by his great grandfather. Finally and with great respect he unwound the ties of the palm leaf manuscript, inscribed with the ancient lore of elephant care. Etched into the dried and hardened leaf was a drawing of the *nila*, (nerve points) on an elephant. The leaves of text tell of elephant castes, prayers and charms. Inspired by the text, Sumanabanda closed his eyes and broke into gentle song. The tones were hypnotic, placid. It was the song that he sings as he walks his elephant to the temple ceremonies. With the song the elephant is calmed. Sometimes he plays his flute. 'They like the flute. They move to the music'.

But the affable manner of this man, whose life is so inextricably linked with elephants, was tinged with desperation. The line is broken. All the treasured objects are, in reality, vestiges of a disappearing culture. Sumanabanda is not prepared however to let his traditions die. It is the custom of mahouts to pass on their skills and knowledge to their sons. Sumanabanda has no son. Instead he is teaching his young sister the ways of the mahout. She may well become the first female mahout in history.

Mr Sumanabanda's knowledge of elephants is vast. From the sound of an elephant, from its saliva, its droppings, its gait and the look in its eyes he can tell much about the elephant's diet, its strength and its general wellbeing. In his journey through life the elephant is his reason for being. It is not only his friend and his vehicle, it is also his map, providing him with an orientation from the past to the future.

SIX

RITUAL
AND
CEREMONY

THE PERAHERA
PROCESSION

HROUGHOUT Sri Lanka, ceremonies and festivities are regularly held to commemorate important events or to invoke blessings for success and prosperity. Some of these festivities are steeped in over 2,500 years of tradition. Some rituals have an unbroken lineage. Invariably an event of any significance will include elephants. If the event is linked with abundant harvests, rain and fertility, then the presence of elephants is particularly profound, given their symbolic association with such fortune. At these celebrations up to 100 splendidly and colourfully attired elephants may parade. Such a procession is called a *perahera*.

> *In the peraheras, the elephants represent the rain clouds; [while] the drums and the music [represent] the noise of thunder and water.*[150]

There are many different *peraheras* throughout Sri Lanka. At Kelaniya, ten kilometres east of Colombo, the *Duruthu perahera* in January commemorates the Buddha's visit to that locale. The February full moon is the time for the *Navam perahera* at the Gangaramaya Temple in Colombo. *Wesak* in May celebrates the Buddha's enlightenment, and *Poson* in June honours the arrival of Buddhism on the island. In August the Kataragama God rides atop an elephant in a *perahera* to visit his lover Valli.

Perhaps the best known of the *peraheras* is the one held in Kandy in July/August, the *Esala perahera*. To appreciate the profound nature of this festival, it is worth looking into the history of Kandy, the home of *Sri Dalada*, the Sacred Tooth Relic of the Buddha.

At celebrations held regularly throughout Sri Lanka, up to 100 elaborately adorned elephants may parade amidst hundreds of drummers and dancers. Such a parade is known as a perahera.

The King's Palace at Kandy

This illustration by Lt. William T. Lyttleton (1819), depicts
the King's Palace and Temple complex housing the Sacred
Tooth Relic of the Buddha in Kandy.

Kandy

NSCONCED in the lush hill country in central Sri Lanka is Kandy, the cultural and spiritual capital of the island. Four hundred years ago this city became the political centre chosen by the Sinhalese kings as they fled the rule of the Portuguese in the low country. The subsequent kings maintained a fierce independence against continued waves of colonial invasion from the Portuguese, the Dutch and then the British.

Finally, in 1815, the British succeeded in taking Kandy in what is said to have been the most formidable insurrection of the whole of the British colonial period in Sri Lanka. The city remained under British rule until independence in 1948.

As the city that houses the famous Sacred Tooth Relic of the Buddha, Kandy attains a symbolic sovereignty over the whole island and serves as a magnet for devotees of Buddhism from around the world.

In keeping with Buddhist custom, relics or remains of the Buddha are highly revered as a symbolic representation of the living Buddha. As such they become a focus for ceremony. In Sri Lanka, no relic has been so highly exalted as the Sacred Tooth Relic, which arrived on the island from India in the fourth century AD. In the 1,600 years since the Tooth Relic arrived, the rulers of Sri Lanka have taken extraordinary measures to protect it from falling into the hands of adversaries.

In 1592 the relic was installed in a shrine in Kandy. Over the next 300 years it was removed many times to protect it from the waves of colonial invasion. Finally, in 1853, 38 years after the British took Kandy, the rights to the temple and the sacred relics were handed back to the Kandyans, restoring to them not only their most cherished relic but also the status of sovereignty.

On the arrival of the Tooth Relic in Sri Lanka in the fourth century AD, the king decreed that it would be publicly displayed in a great annual ceremony. Today this is commemorated as the *Esala* (July/August) *perahera*, one of the most celebrated and colourful festivals in all of Asia. Although now seen primarily as a Sinhala Buddhist festival, the origins of the *perahera* are deeply embedded in Hindu practice and mythology. The original purpose of the *Esala* festival was to invoke the gods for fertility, rain and abundant crops, so essential to sustaining life on the island. Indeed the Tooth Relic itself is believed to have rain making power and its Custodian, *Diyawadana Nilame* ('water increasing minister')[151] is the most significant person charged with the responsibility for the *Esala* ceremonies. These days the festival coincides with the end of a dry season in Sri Lanka and many still attribute the subsequent rains to the *perahera*.

Today the *perahera* reveals a complex synthesis of both Hindu and Buddhist practice, with participants from the Buddhist temple and the shrines of Kandy's four deities.

Every night, just on dusk, drummers, horn blowers, dancers, fire walkers and whip crackers accompany elaborately adorned elephants in procession. Prominent in the procession is the holy tusker. He carries the golden casket housing the Buddha's relics.

The Esala Perahera
The Procession in Kandy

It is dawn in Kandy.

The air is still and cool but it already offers a hint of the heat to come.

The sun casts its first light across the lake, illuminating *Sri Dalada Maligawa*, the temple which houses the Sacred Tooth Relic of the Buddha. With majesty and solemnity it stands watch over the lake and the town stretching from its shores.

The dawn silence is suddenly interrupted by the poignant reverberations of the conch shell. For 1,700 years this daily ritual has announced the auspicious moment that begins the *aluyam tevava* ritual drawing people to make their offerings of rice and flowers. Within the echo of the conch, the music of the temple drummers and horn blowers is strangely shrill, yet consonant. Inside the vast arched walls, the sound is piercing. Outside it travels far, as it lures more and more people to morning rituals.

Today is no ordinary day. Tonight is the night of the August full moon, the final night of the *Esala Mangalle*, the 11 day festival, which honours Buddhism and invokes the blessings of the gods for rain, fertility, successful crops and good health. Tonight 100 lavishly dressed elephants, these *earthly clouds and symbols of abundance and fertility*, will parade. As they have done for the nine preceding nights, they will move within a sea of colour, serenaded by pulsating drums and haunting music.

On a hill to the side of the temple, the elephants graze, seemingly oblivious to the evening's activities. Most have journeyed long distances, often for some days, usually at night to avoid excessive heat and traffic. To see an elephant with its mahout negotiating early morning traffic on the road to a *perahera* is to see, in one frame, the monumental contrasts of modern Sri Lanka. A healthy spirited elephant with head held high, a keen stride and a straight back rising above the vehicles is a triumph of tradition and spiritual values over materialistic folly. But some elephants are weak and clearly struggling to reach their destination. With sagging muscles, lowered head, sunken eyes and a slovenly gait these elephants are all but consumed by the angry metal and belching fumes of the vehicles that surround them. They appear defeated and they are pathetic reminders of the possible destiny of *Elephas maximus*.

Now, having reached their destination they graze quietly.

In a small office, almost tunnelled beneath the side of the temple, Mr Bandaranayake, Private Secretary, issues final orders. For months he has laboured over the arrangements, ensuring sufficient shelter, food and water for the multitudes of drummers, dancers, fire walkers, mahouts and elephants.

Huge elephant tusks arch the plush interior of the Sri Dalada Maligawa, the Temple which houses the Sacred Tooth Relic of the Buddha. Brought to Sri Lanka in the fourth century AD, it is the most revered relic in the nation. Kandy, the city in which the relic resides, therefore attains symbolic sovereignty over the entire island.

On the hill the elephants continue to feed, at times scraping the grass with their feet, then passing it to their mouths with their trunks. Some crush the small logs delivered to them each day for lunch. Others, with trunks stretched high into the tree canopy remove and relish a tasty morsel from a palm. They are all tethered to their spot. Young ones stay close to their mothers. Most are oblivious to the odd tourist who wanders up the hill to stand quietly and observe. Some are untethered by their mahouts and led to the grounds in front of the temple. There, they perform in front of curious and bemused tourists, while their mahouts eagerly await the expected tip. Small boys offer plaited bracelets for sale. Elephant hair they say is very auspicious. The tourists buy, innocent of the possibility that their purchase may not be the presumed elephant hair, but rather fibre of the kitul palm.

It is mid afternoon, and time for the elephant dressing to begin. Each elephant is led slowly down the hill, past the Vishnu Devale. In Sri Lanka, the deity Vishnu is one of the protectors of Buddhism. Some believe he is also Lord of the Elephants.

As they descend the narrow stairs the elephants carefully balance their huge bulk. They assume the appropriate angle while still grasping their lunch of kitul palm. They arrive at the high wall on the western side of the Temple of the Sacred Tooth near the entrance. Here they form a line, as if continuing the elephant statues which grace the temple entrance. The area is transformed into a giant elephant change room. Each elephant places its food in front and slowly munches as the dressing proceeds.

Whilst getting dressed, two elephants 'reassure one another'.

Dresses seem to arrive from nowhere. The elephants stand patiently as mahouts clamber over them draping and attaching the dress that will cover the main body, the ears and the trunk. Only the eyes will peek through. One elephant extends its trunk to another as if in reassurance. A curious trunk may reach under and up a colleague's dress and is deterred only by a sharp word from the mahout.

Fully cloaked in sequined velvet of rich deep blues, exotic ambers and vibrant reds, the elephants form a cascade of colour against the temple wall. With their mahouts they wait calmly and patiently for the sun to go down and the ceremony to begin. People mull around. Security tightens. Loudspeakers perched high in the tree tops transmit banal echoes from the local radio station. It is a time when mahouts must be particularly alert. They must ensure that their elephant does not ruffle its dress. And they must keep the elephant calm amidst a swelling crowd and a cacophony of fireworks, drumming, and whip cracking. Some elephants may be experiencing their first festival. These will require particular scrutiny.

The tusker that carries the relics is dressed separately. From an elevated platform the relic casket is carefully lowered onto his back.

It is late afternoon. The sky softens. The temple lights are lit. The entire building and surrounding trees are bathed in a mist of pink and gold.

Despite the obvious security and the collective knowing that something of significance and meaning is about to occur, there is an air of serenity. This pageant, ancient and awesome, will begin at the time prescribed by the astrologers and it will proceed this year just as it has for thousands of years.

Instantly the air is rent by a sharp piercing crack. The auspicious moment has arrived. The ceremony may begin.

Muscular, barefooted, bare-chested men in white sarongs lead the procession. Their bodies follow the whirling of the whips to a meeting with the ground in a deafening crack. Next, upright and with pomp, the bearers of the region's flags parade. Behind them the first elephant, huge and regal, in thick heavy elaborate gown, moves slowly forward. This first elephant carries the *Peramune Rala*, the dignitary with the temple's tenant and property records. He is dressed in the traditional apparel of the noble.

The drummers, in their white sarongs, red cummerbunds and turban-like headwear, pound alluring rhythms at a frenetic pace.

Brilliantly arrayed, a magnificent tusker carries the *Gajanayake Nilame*, gripping his silver ankus. Traditionally this noble gentleman was the Head of the Royal Elephant Stables.

Gaily decorated dancers with necklets, bracelets and anklets move to the rhythms of the drums and horn blowers. Elaborately adorned elephants, in rows of three sway to the beat. At times, with their trunks linked or tucked away they are almost dancing. Flanking the entire procession are the men with fire. They wield large wooden poles topped with flames that soar high into the air. At regular intervals they lower their poles 're-fuelling' them with coconut shells. The heat is intense. Sweat from their bodies pours to the ground and mixes with the smouldering cinders of the coconuts.

Right: Mr Neranjan Wijeratne, Diyawadana Nilame, Lay Custodian of the Temple of The Sacred Tooth Relic, is primarily responsible for the activities of the Kandy festival. The ten day festival, which may involve more than 100 elephants, concludes during the July/August full moon.

Temple officials with the *Kariya Korala*, Master of Ceremonies, drift past.

Smoke plays tricks with the coloured lights.

Then proudly and majestically, attended by numerous officials and flanked by two radiant tuskers, the sacred *Maligawa Tusker* appears resplendent. A huge and colourful canopy crowns the golden domed relic casket on his back. He is showered with jasmine, as the royal white *pawada* cloth is spread before him. He moves across it. Never do his feet touch the naked ground.

With his ministers and village chiefs the *Diyawadana Nilame* (Lay Custodian to the Sacred Tooth Temple), follows the sacred tusker. As the holder of the most esteemed lay office, he is dressed in the ancient regalia of the kings, and attended ceremoniously by parasol and leaf bearers. He walks at a slow deliberate pace. He gazes straight ahead.

The procession continues with elephants, dancers, drummers and musicians. The *Basnayaka Nilames*, the custodians from each of Kandy's *devales* (shrines to the deities), follow in turn. First is the section honouring God Natha, the benevolent god and considered to be the next Buddha. Following is the procession honouring God Vishnu, protector of Buddhism in Sri Lanka. The Kataragama procession, honouring one of the most popular gods on the island is next, and finally the procession for the Goddess Pattini who is deeply cherished as the goddess of purity, chastity and health.

Sometimes the procession halts. The drummers form a circle, the horn blowers play to the crowd and the dancers move faster. The elephants adjust quickly to the pace.

The elephants remain unperturbed by the heat, the flames, the shrill sounds of the horns and the spirited movements of the dancers. Several men run behind scooping elephant droppings into a sack.

With a final parade around the perimeter of the old city the *perahera* comes once again to the *Sri Dalada Maligawa*. There it concludes.

The next day the final rituals are performed. Before dawn, the *cutting of the water* at an appointed place on the river near Peradeniya, symbolises rain-making. Special ceremonies are conducted at the Ganesha Kovil, the shrine of the elephant headed god. And at the Vishnu Devale a dance is performed in front of the elephant dress to offset any wrong doing which may have occurred during the festivities. Subsequently the *Nilames* (custodians) visit the President's pavilion in Kandy. There they report that according to tradition the rites of the *Esala Mangalle* have been enacted and completed.

For the next few days the roads from Kandy carry the elephants returning to their villages and their work. Perhaps they know that once again they have performed their symbolic duties. Thus, as the clouds that walk the earth they have been instrumental in attracting the vital rains and the nation can look forward to abundant harvests, health and prosperity.[152]

The Legend of Raja
The Maligawa Tusker

ශ්‍රී දළද මාලිගාවේ "රාජා" හස්තියා
"ராஜா" ஸ்ரீ தலதா மாளிகையின் தந்த யானை
"RAJA" TUSKER OF SRI DALADA MALIGAWA

ON FULL moon nights, in the eastern jungles near Batticaloa, the fish are said to sing. There, in about 1922, a tusker was born. He belonged to the Mangala caste; the caste with large physique, eyes like a cormorant's, spotted trunk and white nails. They are arrogant, but harmless.

However, this tusker's destiny was not as a wild elephant roaming freely in those eastern jungles. Rather, he was to become the renowned *Dalada Maligawa Tusker*, the tusker of the Temple of the Sacred Tooth Relic. He would win the hearts and minds of the entire nation of Lanka. The *Diyawadana Nilame*, the lay custodian of the Buddha's Tooth Relic, a position akin to a Buddhist Chieftain, would speak of him as if he were a family member. A postage stamp would be issued bearing his image. The President of the land would declare him a national treasure. On his death a nation would mourn and a museum would be constructed in his honour.

In 1925, in the village of Giragama, west of Kandy in the central hills, a devout man was considering his aspiration to attain Buddhahood. The man was Tikiri Bandara Mampitiye, the Disawe (Governor) of Yatinuwara. His plan was to acquire two tuskers and, in the tradition of the Buddha, give them both to the Temple of the Sacred Tooth Relic. He hoped they would become the bearers of the relics of the Buddha in the Kandy *perahera*. At this moment, the fate of the young tusker in the Batticaloa jungles became inextricably linked with the vision of the Disawe to reach his Nirvana (enlightenment).

In collaboration with his sister, Mampitiye Rambukpotha, Tikiri Bandara proceeded with his intentions. Expressing the wish to obtain two baby tuskers, the same size, was easier than fulfilling it. Tuskers were rare in Sri Lanka. Knowing this, the Disawe and his staff initiated a number of lengthy and complex religious rituals that would facilitate the search. Monks, high priests and astrologers were consulted. The entire community became involved with ceremonies of chanting and recitals of Buddhist teachings. Every thought and deed was purified and blessed. All united in devotional acts to appease the gods. And all did so willingly. For devout Buddhists, to participate in the realisation of one's Nirvana, was indeed a privilege.

For centuries, skilful Moormen, Pannikers, had undertaken elephant capture in Sri Lanka. Their courage and expertise were renowned. The Disawe's wish was conveyed to them. Finally the gods showed favour. Two baby tuskers, each one and a half metres in height, were trapped in the Batticaloa jungles.

The Disawe's household buzzed with excitement. The extraordinary event of trapping two tuskers, with the required attributes, within a week of each other reinforced the belief that the gods had sanctioned and blessed the operation. The two were purchased for a total 3,000 rupees ($AUS100), a large sum in those days.

The little elephants journeyed by train to their new home. A huge crowd gathered to meet them, impatient to see the new arrivals. But initially the little tuskers were not to be seen. They were fast asleep in a hay pile and had to be coaxed to face their reception. Amongst the crowd was the Disawe's domestic elephant. She mothered them and they toddled behind her in procession with all the townspeople.

The young elephants were named Raja and Kanda. They were treated like pets in the Disawe's household. They played amongst the nutmeg trees, bathed regularly and received frequent treats of bananas and jaggery (syrup from the kitul palm). They were trained with loving care. They were given special attention from the adult elephant who developed a strong protective instinct toward them.

On 22 August 1937, at the age of 15 and each standing two metres tall, Raja and Kanda were given in *puja*, (offering), to the *Dalada Maligawa*, (the Sacred Tooth Temple). Dressed in fine white silk they moved slowly in procession, with customary dancers and musicians to the temple. There they knelt with their trunks extended in the hands of a senior monk. To the sounds of chanting and horn blowing, water was poured over their trunks, which were then placed in the hands of the *Diyawadana Nilame*, the lay custodian. From that day Raja and Kanda remained in the custody of the appointed *Diyawadana Nilame*. Many thousands of people attended the ceremony, their worshipping chants of 'Sadhu, Sadhu' (Blessed, Blessed) reverberating throughout the temple and the streets of Kandy.

Raja and Kanda began their role in the *Esala perahera* by simply being two of the many elephants in the procession. Eventually they worked their way to a position of rank where they would flank the main tusker carrying the relics. By 1948 a replacement tusker was required. Whilst both Raja and Kanda had been trained to undertake the honourable task, it was Raja who, because of the straightness of his back, became the main bearer. It was in his role as bearer of the giant golden casket, housing the sacred relics, that Raja emanated that special essence which captured the hearts and minds of not only Sri Lankans but also international observers. Raja's skill, dignity and dedication were apparent. His majestic and stately manner generated the conviction that he knew and understood his role to be of the highest order, his purpose divine.

On nights of the *perahera*, Raja would stand still and serene, whilst others fussed about to dress and prepare him. With the preparations complete, he would assume a demeanour of nobility, magnificent in his lavish red velvet dress, fringed in gold and shimmering with lights and sequins. Atop his back was the resplendent golden casket, containing the precious relics of the Buddha. Garlanded in jasmine, with tusks adorned in gold and feet bedecked in silver anklets, Raja stood on the temple steps and bowed to the chants of 'Sadhu, Sadhu'.

Being the most honoured tusker, a *pawada*, or white cloth, was laid before him on which to walk. If the laying was delayed, he would wait patiently, sometimes holding his forefoot off the ground until the *pawada* was properly positioned. At times he would offer his trunk in assistance. For the duration of the *perahera*, he moved with grace and solemnity, taking prominence in the long procession of elephants, dignitaries, dancers, drummers, flag bearers and whip crackers. With the *perahera* concluded, he approached the temple descending into a low prostration. Witnesses insist that he did this of his own volition, because he knew and understood the profound nature of the temple and his task.

When young, Raja was not without a sense of mischief. On occasions he attacked vehicles. Many still remember a particular incident of Raja's rage. He stormed down the road threatening vehicles and passers by. Nothing and no-one seemed to be immune from his fury. Having terrorised one village, charging vehicles and small shops he proceeded to the next. But suddenly he stopped. He was standing in the street in front of an elderly beggar. The old man prostrated in worship. Gently, with his trunk, Raja picked up the man. Carrying him to one side of the road he placed him, with utmost delicacy on the ground.

However fervent Raja's outbursts, the mahouts were always able to calm him. They would visit one, or all four, of Kandy's *devales*, (deities), asking for Raja's protection. His aggression never lost him esteem and affection. People of every faith honoured him.

Raja matured into a serene elephant. The respect and warmth toward him deepened and he became an ambassador for Sri Lanka. His fame extended and visitors came from around the world. A new industry in carved images of the revered elephant exploded as Raja's popularity grew. Sri Lankans were appreciative of the ambassadorial and economic benefits brought by the elephant. But more than this, they regarded Raja as a symbol of the spirit and culture of their land. As Buddhists, many believed, that to be entrusted with such momentous responsibilities, Raja must have attained extraordinary merit by charitable deeds in his former life. They deeply cherished the notion that he was linked with the ultimate goal in Buddhism, the goal of enlightenment, in this case, that of the Disawe's.

In May 1985, His Excellency, President Jayewardene declared Raja a national treasure.

The current *Diyawadana Nilame*, Mr Neranjan Wijeyeratne, had a long and close association with Raja. This began in 1974 when, as a young child, his father was the Nilame. 'I grew up with Raja', he said, relating his memories:

> *One year, in the middle of the perahera, Raja suddenly stopped. He refused to budge. No amount of encouragement would entice him to move. People around him became concerned. A perahera with the holy tusker refusing to participate would be a catastrophe. On close inspection, the mahout discovered that a strap supporting the howdah was lose. If Raja had moved the whole casket may have capsised. To have the sacred relics of Buddha crash to the ground would have brought trauma to the entire nation. With the strap adjusted, Raja went forward to undertake his esteemed role for another year.*

Mr Wijeyeratne also recalled the time when:

> *In 1986, Raja was dressed with the casket carefully placed upon his back. The perahera was ready to begin. Suddenly Raja's mahout fell ill and was taken to hospital. 'What could we do?' said the Nilame. 'The casket was on top and the elephant was ready but no mahout! The other mahouts were reluctant to go too close to Raja'.*

> *The Nilame's trust and affection for the elephant directed his decision. Raja would carry the casket alone. Normally this would be a high risk undertaking. An unaccompanied elephant amidst the noise and crowds of a perahera, with no mahout to reassure him, could spell disaster. But Raja had always performed his duties to perfection. On this day he did not disappoint. 'Raja was fantastic' the Nilame said, recalling the episode as though it were yesterday. 'He knew exactly what to do and he did it for three and a half hours. When he finished I gave him a big bunch of bananas, cooled him down and led him slowly to a tree'.*

Raja became seriously ill in March 1988. Dr V. Kuruwita, Head of the Department of Veterinary Clinical Studies at the University of Peradeniya, administered drugs and an intravenous drip. Teams of doctors and helpers stayed with the sick elephant 24 hours a day to monitor his condition and offer support. Thousands of well wishers from all over Sri Lanka gathered at Raja's 'bedside'. Their numerous gifts of fruit, medicines, flowers and jaggery, necessitated the allocation of a special room for storage.

One day Raja collapsed. Although he tried desperately to stand he was too weak to lift his massive 4,000 kilo body. An elephant that lies down for too long will develop breathing difficulties and eventually die. It was therefore imperative that Raja be placed in a standing position.

Dr Kuruwita made what he regards as the most important decision of his professional career. He organised a massive lifting operation. A tunnel was built under the fallen elephant and a rope was passed around his body. This was attached to a 40 tonne crane which lifted the elephant into a specially constructed crate designed to help him stay upright. The risk of internal injury and trauma was very high and the operation required precision planning and co-ordination.

The manoeuvre was a success. Following a full recovery Raja was able to participate in two more processions: *Wesak*, Buddha's Birthday in May, and *Poson* in June, the commemoration of the arrival of Buddhism to Sri Lanka.

Raja spent his last days in the garden of Mr Wijeyeratne's home. A special pool was constructed for his daily bath.

The time of the *Esala perahera* was drawing near. Knowing that Raja may not be well enough to carry the casket, the *Nilame* sought a replacement bearer, a tusker, also called Raja from Ratnapura, near the mountain of Sri Pada in the south. The new tusker arrived at the *Nilame's* residence on 15 July so that the two elephants could meet. At 10.20 the next morning, after a hearty breakfast, at the age of 65, Raja died. The official diagnosis was cardiac failure.

'He had met the new bearer of the relics. He knew now that he could go' said Mr Wijeyeratne, holding back tears. 'Raja is still close to me. It was like losing a family member, because from 1975 I was growing up with him'.

The famous *Maligawa Tusker* now lies in Mr Wijeyeratne's garden, beneath a tombstone built to honour him.

Immediately following Raja's death many thousands of people flocked to Mr Wijeyeratne's Kandy residence to honour the creature they loved and respected so much. Lying on a bed of leaves and covered in gold brocade, with jasmine garlanding his tusks, Raja even in death had not lost the majesty he had exuded in life.

In a simple ceremony Raja was administered the last rites.

The stories of Raja are immortalised in a museum adjacent to the *Maligawa*. The entire museum is dedicated to the tusker, and to the memories of his cherished life.

From detailed measurements of his entire body a frame was built over which his preserved skin was stretched. His life-like image now stands prominent in the museum, a final and lasting testament to his almost half century of service to the Buddha and to the people of Sri Lanka.[153]

For almost 50 years, Raja, the revered elephant of the Kandy Temple carried the relics of the Buddha on his back in the festivals and processions. In December 1989, 18 months after his death, a commemorative stamp was issued to honour Raja and his years of service to the temple and to the people of Sri Lanka.

Another Raja?

'There will never be another Raja'. This is the universal cry of those who knew Raja, who grew up with him and who watched him every year as he carried the relics of Buddha with such an appropriate sense of importance. It is true. There never will be another Raja. Much like people, elephants are individuals. Each is unique.

But there have been many elephants since Raja's death which have carried the relics with suitable aplomb. One belongs to Mr Henry Gunasekara, a Kandy businessman. This large 55 year-old tusker is also named Raja. His tusks are magnificently curved.

This Raja his carried the Tooth Relic on several occasions. He has also assumed the privileged positions of bearer of the *Peramune Rala*, the man who delivers the mandate for the *perahera*, and bearer of the *Gajanayake Nilame*, the traditional keeper of the king's elephants.

With his noble attributes and broad experience, maybe he or a similar elephant will be a successor to Raja, the *Maligawa Tusker*.

Mr Neranjan Wijeratne grew up with the famous tusker, Raja. Raja's grave assumes a prominent position in the garden of Mr Wijeratne's Kandy home.

A City Park
Temporary Home to 130 Elephants

*I*F A *perahera* is a spectacularly coloured creature snaking a path from the temple, then the elephants are its giant backbone providing stability, strength and stature.

Nowhere are the mechanics of organising a *perahera* more visible than in the Viharamahadevi Park, in the heart of Colombo. During the Colombo *perahera* up to 130 elephants are stabled in this park. Provision of food and water, removal of dung and general welfare of elephants and mahouts is the responsibility of the priests of the Gangaramaya Temple.

The influx of elephants begins as a trickle. On the day before the *perahera* the large park swarms with water trucks, officials, curious tourists, even more curious locals and, of course, elephants. Yet the atmosphere is one of serenity rather than chaos. The elephants are young and old, male and female, fit and tired. Each one has an allocated position, usually close to a large shade tree. During the daylight hours they stay near their tree doing what elephants do: eating, swaying, relishing the regular watering. Occasionally they try other activities. Dismantling light posts, overturning buckets and pinching food are not beyond their repertoire.

The *Navam perahera* lasts for two nights only. In the early morning of the first day the elephants are taken along the three kilometre circuit to familiarise them with the route and to receive blessings. Their journey takes them from the Viharamahadevi Park, past the Gangaramaya Temple and along the city roads back to the park. At the temple each mahout brings his elephant to a halt underneath a balcony from where a priest blesses both man and animal by sprinkling them with holy water.

The same priest then offers a pineapple to the elephant. With an extended trunk the elephant retrieves the blessed fruit. Some elephants devour their pineapple immediately. Others balance the fruit in the tip of their trunk as they continue their journey, preferring to eat it further along the way. One elephant walked all the way back to the park with her pineapple still intact. She delicately placed the pineapple on the ground and had a drink. Then, at the command of her mahout she showered herself. Only when she had completed her ablutions did she pick up her pineapple. She turned her body away from the onlookers to face the tree where she was tied and slowly she devoured and savoured the fruit. For her it was an intensely private experience.

There is always someone watching the elephants. If the mahout is sleeping his assistant will be alert. Sometimes, in the heat of the day, the elephants might also sleep. One mahout commanded his elephant to lie down. 'Hida' he yelled. The large female slowly bent her knees until her stomach met the ground. She then rocked herself until she had developed sufficient momentum to roll her massive body to one side. The mahout stretched himself out on top of her, carefully moulding his lean frame around her contours. Placing his ankus alongside her he promptly fell asleep. The elephant curled her trunk on the ground, closed her eyes and also seemed to sleep. The only movement was a gentle stirring of dust as the sleeping elephant expelled air through her trunk. For one hour, both elephant and mahout remained in that position.

Inside the park is an enormous administration tent, with 130 wooden crates, each containing an elephant dress. On arrival a mahout queues for registration and is issued a key to one of the wooden crates. In addition, each mahout receives his reward for participation in the *perahera*. Every year the reward is different. It has ranged from bicycles to gold medallions. One year the reward was a sewing machine. That year, at the culmination of the festivities, Colombo residents were treated to the sight of more than 100 elephants, sewing machines on their backs, negotiating the city exit routes back to their villages.

Making the Elephant Dress

To make a dress for an elephant is to contribute to an ancient and honoured tradition. Over the centuries dresses used in festivals have been made by villagers, families of mahouts and elephant owners.

From their clothing store in Kandy, Mr and Mrs Thadhani sell garments to people. From their home they make dresses for elephants. These they donate to temples. Their work includes dresses for the special tusked elephant entrusted to carry the sacred relics. 'It's our way of contributing to an important tradition'. They have been contributing to this tradition for over 25 years.

The elephant dress, comprising four layers, requires almost 120 metres of material. The top layer is usually velvet. It takes six people five months to work the cloth into a finished garment. Once completed, it requires more than one person to lift it.

The dress may last four to five years depending on weather conditions during the *perahera*, storage and careful maintenance.

When the Thadhanis have completed an elephant dress they deliver it to the temple. There they participate in a special *puja* (offering), before the dress is ceremoniously placed on the elephant. The elephant wearing a Thadhani dress in a procession moves with the Thadhani name emblazoned across its front; a concession perhaps to modern day advertising practices.

Most elephants that received the blessed fruit, devoured it immediately. This one carried it for some kilometres to a quiet spot where she drank, washed, turned her back and consumed her pineapple in privacy.

The Thadhani Elephant Dress

The elephant dress consists of four layers:

1 A grey lining sheet
2 Poplin lining
3 Foam rubber
4 The outer layer of velvet

There are three main parts to the dress:

† The body section – three by six metres
† The head and trunk piece – two by two metres
† Two ear pieces

Sequins, brocade and pearls are stitched onto the fabric, which is edged with tassels.

For over 25 years Mr and Mrs Thadhani have made elephant dresses. This is their way of contributing to a time honoured tradition.

Organising a perahera is a mammoth task in logistics and requires patience. The Venerable Gala Boda Gnanissara, High Priest of the Gangaramaya Buddhist Temple in Colombo, was the right man for the job.

The Priest and the Elephant

He was lean and agile. His youthful features belied his years. His eyes were sharp but not uninviting. In his right hand he clutched a mobile phone. His overall disposition was akin to a stockbroker on the floor of the exchange. But this broker wore orange robes. He was the Venerable Gala Boda Gnanissara, the popular and dynamic High Priest of the Gangaramaya Buddhist Temple in the heart of Colombo.

He was immersed in a dizzying schedule, supervising the preparations for the annual Colombo, *Navam perahera*, (Procession) of the February full moon. But one sensed that even without a festival to organise, he would move at this frenetic pace. It was still four weeks before the two day festival where 130 elephants and hundreds of performers would parade before many thousands of spectators.

With minimal discussion he assumed, quite correctly, the purpose of our visit. 'It's crucial that we protect the elephants. I will help you'. He spoke clearly, expelling his words rapidly and with a great sense of urgency.

We followed him as he moved briskly about the temple, his robes trailing in a struggle to keep up. All the while he sustained a monologue into his mobile phone, interrupted only to issue orders to the numerous orange-robed priests and other festival organisers. Trucks were unloading, workers required directions, documents demanded signatures, stands needed erecting, mahouts and elephants required food and water. The Venerable Gnanissara was in his domain. He was clearly in control.

We wanted to ask him about his temple elephants. We wanted to hear his elephant stories and we wanted to know more about his preparations for the *perahera*. But even as we posed our questions he continued talking into his phone. The only word we could understand, and one he uttered regularly, was 'aliya'.

Suddenly we were ushered into a small room in the heart of the temple complex. 'You must have some tea' he said, before quickly disappearing. We sat in silence and wondered if that was it? Would we see him again? Would our questions be answered?

Moments later an old man shuffled into the room. He carried a tray with the ubiquitous pot of tea, two delicate china cups and six carefully arranged slices of fruit cake. He smiled without saying anything, placed the tray on a wooden table and then left.

We sipped our tea in silence as we absorbed the cluttered strangeness of the room. One wall was dominated with a vast wooden and glass bookcase filled with ancient palm leaf manuscripts and a curious mix of foreign language books. A shelf on another wall supported a pair of mounted elephant tusks that formed a canopy over a gaudy clock with English chimes. Framed black and white photographs of Buddhist ordinations hung alongside colour pictures of temple elephants. And numerous icons of the Buddha were dotted about the room. We sat there for perhaps 15 minutes, our unanswered questions somewhat eclipsed by the comfort of the room, the hot tea and sweet cake.

Suddenly Venerable Gnanissara burst through the door. He was still clutching his mobile phone. 'The elephants have arrived' he announced. Without warning he dashed to the opposite end of the room, where he flung open the double wooden doors that led onto an outside courtyard. But instead of an open yard, we found ourselves only inches away from a magnificent elephant with enormous crossed tusks.

We stood stunned at the image before us. Within seconds we had traversed from an English afternoon tea to this grand and beautiful creature, with well rounded protruding domes on his forehead and small eyes beneath. His thick trunk with perfect pink markings fell with ease to the ground. His slender tusks curved forward before crossing at the tips. Even in the low light, they gleamed. He took a firm but gentle stance, his small ears flapping intermittently. Beside him stood two slightly smaller elephants. At the command of the mahout the tusker knelt before the High Priest. The Venerable Gnanissara patted the elephant on the forehead. He fed bunches of bananas into cavernous mouths while sustaining a dialogue on his mobile phone, issuing orders and responding to questions of his staff as they scuttled about the labyrinthine temple.

The Priest made a brisk gesture to the mahout. The elephants turned and were gone. And soon the Priest was also gone. 'I've arranged for Dr Kodikara to come. He's the vet for our elephants. He'll tell you many things', he said as he disappeared to meet a delegation from Canada.

THE MYSTERIES
OF KATARAGAMA

Invocation to the Lord Kataragama

Kataragama has given alms and has acquired merit from previous births
There is no one to match him on this earth
[Banish] all types of dosa (troubles) of humans living in this world
O Kataragama, chief of the army [of gods], give us victory.

With pearl umbrella unfurled he rides his golden peacock
And constantly makes wishes...for future Buddhahood
I, your servant...sing songs...on this occasion
How we worship Prince Skanda...[154]

IN THE south east of Sri Lanka, in the small sacred town of Kataragama, a puzzling and mysterious air lingers. Throughout the year tens of thousands of devotees of all faiths are drawn to this place. But at first the flat, hot and dusty town seems alienating and unfriendly. Young cowboys soliciting outrageous prices for jeep tours of the nearby Yala National Park dominate the main street. To bolster their own business they spread rumours that malign their neighbours and competitors. This place seems anything but sacred.

But like so many things in Sri Lanka, the surface is rarely the reality. In the centre of Kataragama the huge fenced park with lush green grass and shady trees exudes an inviting serenity. People are drawn from the monotonous heat and dust on the other side. Pilgrims filter steadily through the partially opened gate. At the river, devotees purify their bodies before attending the *puja* (offering).

This sanctuary is a cross roads where many faiths intersect. At the end of the wide tree-lined street a mosque, Hindu shrines and a Buddhist thupa stand in testimony to this rich convergence.

Primarily, this is the area of the god Skanda, known also as Murugan, Kadira, Kandapata, Mahasen, Subramanya and the Kataragama god. His popularity is such that he is regarded by some as the national god of Sri Lanka. His temple stands omnipresent, white and glistening in the hot unrelenting sun. Nearby is the shrine dedicated to his brother Ganesha, the elephant headed god. The area is surrounded by a stone fence of perfectly sculptured black elephants. These symbols of protection stand shiny and sturdy. Peacocks, Skanda's vehicle, adorn the entrance.

It was from this area, the abode of Skanda, that the King Dutugemunu (161–137 BC) is said to have embarked for battle with King Elara. Before leaving he entreated Skanda for help. On his victorious return, he gave thanks to Skanda and built shrines in appreciation.

Opposite: Skanda, also known as Murugan, is the brother of Ganesha, the elephant
headed god. He is the deity of Kataragama. For some, he is the national deity. In this
temple painting at Kataragama he is depicted with his wives, Devasena and Valli.

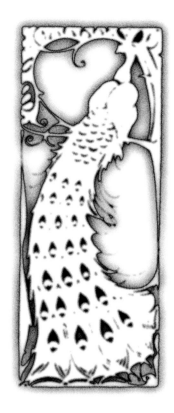

Just as Skanda's names are numerous so too are the stories about his significance and his manifestation in Sri Lanka. Some say Skanda's arrival in Sri Lanka was due to the cunning and later goodwill of his elder brother, Ganesha, the elephant headed god.

One day Parvati said to her two sons, Ganesha and Skanda, that she would give a golden mango to the son who travelled around the universe first. Skanda immediately set off around the world on his vehicle, the peacock. Ganesha thought about his mother's statement considering what she may have meant. Then he proceeded to circle his mother, after which he honoured her by bowing to her and stating 'I have encircled you. You are my universe'. She immediately rewarded him with the golden mango. On his return, Skanda was furious. He left his family and went to the hill overlooking Kataragama.

Soon after his arrival in Kataragama, Skanda fell in love with a beautiful woman called Valli Amma (Mother Valli). He deeply desired her. He changed himself into an old man and appeared to her. She was picking flowers. He was playing his flute. He expressed his love for her. She was repulsed by him. Ganesha, wanting to make amends with his brother, appeared as a wild elephant and frightened Valli to the extent that she pleaded with Skanda to save her. He promised to do so on the condition that she marry him. She reluctantly agreed. When he changed back into his youthful self, she was more than happy.[155]

Each year at the time of *Esala*, the July/August full moon, tens of thousands of people pour into Kataragama. They come to celebrate the nuptials of Skanda and Valli. A sacred box, containing relics and symbolising the god, is placed on the back of a lavishly decorated elephant. At that moment, the elephant raises his trunk and issues a loud trumpet. He then carries the god to his lover, Valli, in a *perahera* where people praise their god with ceremony, ritual and chants.[156]

As the sacred elephant carries the god to his lover, he symbolises the endeavour of the elephant headed god Ganesha, whose actions brought Skanda to Sri Lanka and initiated the relationship between Skanda and Valli.

Whether in its heavenly form as deity or in its earthly animal form, the elephant has been integral to the evolving myths of Kataragama. Today it continues to assume a prominent place as the myths are enacted in the customary rituals.

FOR THE PROTECTION OF THE ELEPHANTS

NOT far from Kegalle, about 70 kilometres east of Colombo, at the end of a narrow dusty track, is the Alutnuwara Temple. It stands secluded on dry flat dust surrounded by expansive gardens. An air of generosity pervades. There is a sense that this place accommodates something of magnitude. Here it is easy to conjure images of hundreds of elephants slowly parading.

This is the place of the deity Dadimunda, the god of this locale. To one side of the huge white temple a small grotto perches high in the rock. This, they say, is where the god came to earth.

Dadimunda, the stern and fearless one, is said to have protected the Buddha from the onslaught of Mara, a force similar to Satan in the Christian world. Whilst every other god deserted the Buddha, Dadimunda stood resolute defeating the demon Mara and his armies of devils. In return the Buddha gave Dadimunda *varan*, a warrant as chief of the devils.[157] Any god who fought single handedly to protect the Buddha, who defeated hosts of devils and who is authorised by the Buddha to rule the demons, must be a powerful god and a god worth beseeching.

Owners and mahouts come here with their elephants to seek protection and blessings. As a newborn, little Puja, the elephant born to the Samarasinghe family, came here. When Raja, the *Maligawa Tusker* was ill or misbehaving, prayers were offered here. And it is here that Mr Sumanabanda, Chief Mahout of the elephant orphanage, brings his own elephant. He cannot bring all the orphans. But he seeks blessings for them by collecting small brass elephant images at the entrance to the temple. He presents these to the priest who officiates in the lush inner sanctum arched by huge and ancient ivory tusks. Their prayers are for the health and safety of all the elephants at the orphanage.

Once a year, just before partaking in the pomp and pageantry of the Kandy *perahera*, the mahouts and elephants of this district come to their god, Dadimunda. They seek his blessings as they engage in their own *perahera* in the seclusion and solitude of his abode.

A wall of elephants offers protection to the four shrines at Kataragama, including the deities Skanda and Ganesha.

Mahouts and owners come to this secluded temple, the abode of the deity Dadimunda, to seek blessings for their elephants.

NEW YEAR
FESTIVITIES

NEW Year in Sri Lanka occurs in the month of *Bak*, March/April. It heralds the beginning of spring and is a celebration of successful harvests. It is a time when families and friends are reconciled, a time for rejoicing and festivities. Music, dancing and even elephant races form part of the revelry.

Elephant Races at Bomiriya near Colombo

Since early morning the crowds grew steadily around the public arena. By midday people were crammed four deep along the perimeter of the hot dusty space. Many climbed high into the trees and balanced themselves precariously for a better view. There was little respite from the blistering sun yet the people waited with astonishing patience.

At one end of the arena was an erected stage with red carpet. Priests, politicians and other dignitaries sat in comfortable chairs and were cooled by electric fans. Two large chairs at centre stage were flanked by a pair of enormous elephant tusks.

Luxury cars stirred the dust as they pulled up abruptly to release yet another official. The crowd swelled and the heat intensified. The celebrations for the Sinhala/Tamil New Year would soon begin. The elephant race was the widely promoted highlight of the day-long festivities. But where were the elephants?

Beyond the edge of the dusty arena, away from the crowd, was a small stretch of woodland. Beneath the shady canopy of the trees 20 elephants, their mahouts and families were resting, eating and waiting.

The friendly chatter of picnicking mahouts was serenaded by a continual and gentle chiming of elephant bells. Above this the occasional command from mahout to elephant was audible. Sometimes one elephant would trumpet and spark a chorus. But mostly the woods were serene.

The first race was scheduled to start at 2 p.m. At 2.30 p.m. the speeches began. The drone of speaker after speaker was amplified across the space and beyond the woods where the elephants waited. A hot wind carried the badly distorted words back to the stage. All the while more dignitaries arrived.

Though it seemed hardly possible, the crowd continued to thicken and the April sun intensified. Suddenly a huge elephant emerged from the woods. The crowd stirred. Was the race about to begin? With its mahout at its side the elephant strolled across the arena, negotiated its way through the bedlam at the far end and exited through the entrance gate. For this elephant and rider, the waiting had become too much.

Eventually the speeches stopped and attention turned to the centre of the arena where a game for children was being played. Each child was blindfolded and asked to 'pin the eye on the elephant drawing'. The children laughed, the crowd applauded and the winner was announced. More games were followed by yet more speeches.

Then the drummers took their position. With three, sometimes four, to a drum they beat a frenzied rhythm while the colours of their saris fused into a swirling rainbow. Still the crowd waited.

The racing of elephants is a
centuries-old tradition.

It was after 5 p.m. when the elephants and their riders finally emerged from the woods and took up ranks at the far end of the arena. Almost before the man with the microphone had finished his frenetic announcements the first race began. The 200 metre event would finish at the foot of the stage in front of the seated dignitaries.

The crowd roared and the dust swirled. With their ears flapping and trunks swinging, five elephants of varying size and age moved with a gentle skip, and, in some cases, a quiet though spirited shuffle. As if to inject ferocity to this gentle scene each mahout, seated erect on his charge, yelled at the top of his voice and pierced the stifling air with the golden tip of his ankus.

Photographers and officials mingling in front of the stage were caught off guard by the elephants that appeared suddenly yet silently from the clouds of dust. Many scattered hurriedly to avoid a collision. But the elephants, ever cautious, successfully dodged the bodies that ran in all directions.

Long before the dust settled and before the elephants in the first race had time to move away, the second race began. Again the mahouts yelled and spirited their charges by thrusting the ankus, like a javelin into the air. Again the crowd roared.

After the fifth and final race it was time for the victors to claim their spoils. The mahouts stood with their charges before the carpeted podium. Each elephant received a bunch of bananas and each mahout an amount of cash. The winner, riding a very young elephant, made a circuit of honour as he carried away his gleaming prize – a two metre brass candelabra.

The day concluded when a huge, lavishly adorned elephant entered the arena. Sitting high on its back the rider was dressed in the traditional and colourful garb of the kings. He presented a scrolled message to the seated dignitaries. Then this distinguished gentleman rode his elephant on a slow but purposeful lap of the arena, issuing New Year blessings to the assembled throng.

SEVEN

ELEPHANT
MANAGEMENT

WHICH WAY FORWARD?

BEFORE the interference of man, elephants managed themselves very well. They had no enemies as they roamed the land along their traditional routes. If they suffered illness, they selected appropriate remedies from the vast natural medicine dispensary within their expansive domain. According to some ecologists, when left alone, elephants lived in harmony with the environment and contributed to an ecological balance.[158] But the expanding human population created competition for territory. Elephants were particularly vulnerable, not just because of their need for large tracts of land, but also because they proved to be such loyal servants to their captors.

The need for protection of the island's flora and fauna has been acknowledged for over 2,000 years. On a wall in Kandy, not far from the Sacred Tooth Temple, is a sign bearing the words of the monk, Mahinda, who brought Buddhism to the land of Lanka. In 306 BC he said:

> *O Great King, the birds of the air and beasts have an equal right to live and move about in any part of this land as thou. The land belong[s] to the people and all other beings. And thou art only the guardian of it.*

In the 12th century, King Kirthi Nissanka Malla of Polonnaruwa issued a decree that:

> *...No animals should be killed within a radius of seven gav [28 miles] from the city.*[159]

However, the king's sentiments did not prevent centuries of exploitation and confrontation that have changed forever the destiny of Sri Lanka's *Elephas maximus maximus*.

At the turn of the 20th century the population of wild elephants was estimated at around 12,000. Today that number is less than 3,000. Many of the wild elephants that have survived now live in pocketed herds. That is, they are trapped by surrounding development. Confrontation with human settlement is therefore inevitable.

The population of domestic elephants is ageing. Given that capture is outlawed and captive breeding is precarious, some fear there may come a time when Sri Lanka no longer has sufficient elephants for its revered festivals. Indeed some also fear the loss of the unique traditions associated with the elephant that are integral to Sri Lankan culture. Such concerns were expressed back in 1969 by A. H. E. Molamure:

> *What of the tradition of elephant lore in Ceylon at the present day? Etiolated beyond recovery, it must wither away in a few years more and with it the phenomenon of the elephant as a tame animal – so integral and so long a part of the life of the island...For, what is required of an elephant today, chiefly if not solely, is a capacity for hard work...elephants in the perahera processions – these are intimations of significance; for one thing, of an increasing inability on our part to live with elephants. The elephant, in fine, is passing out of the ambience of our culture.*[160]

A Never Ending Debate

For decades the following questions have been debated:

 † What is the best way to manage the dwindling elephant population of this tiny island with an expanding human population?

 † How can national parks be developed as havens for wildlife instead of playgrounds for tourists?

 † How many elephants can a particular area sustain?

 † Should intruding elephants be relocated and, if so, how and where?

 † Should additional dams be established to deter elephants from migrating, or

 † Should corridors (pathways along which elephants can safely travel) between the parks be established?

 † Should farmers receive compensation for damaged crops and punishment for shooting an elephant?

All of these questions need answers. As committees are established, inquiries conducted, reports written, recommendations made and more committees established, the elephants continue to die.

What Price Development?

Perhaps nowhere in Sri Lanka is the current plight of the elephants better illustrated than with the Mahaweli project. Since the mid 1960s this multi-billion dollar programme has changed the face of the Mahaweli river basin in the central east of Sri Lanka. Huge dams, extensive electricity grids and diverted rivers have resulted in new industries and settlements in areas that were previously uninhabitable for people. This same project has also displaced substantial numbers of wild elephants.

The new industries have blocked the traditional elephant routes. And new areas of crop production have lured elephants to an abundant food source. To compensate, the government created the Floodplains National Park but industries continue to develop in and around the fertile edges of the park.

Matara Swami

'Just go to Kataragama and ask for him' we were told. 'He'll tell you about elephants'. We searched the large temple complex. 'We're looking for Matara Swami' we said. 'Wait over there' a man directed us to the Vishnu Devale. 'He always arrives there in the afternoon'.

One hour before sunset an old but upright man with alert eyes, a long white beard and a maroon sarong walked towards us. Matara Swami sat cross legged on the hot ground and drew pictures with a stick in the sand. He spoke of how the Veddhas, the aboriginal people of Sri Lanka, understood the elephants. He told us how the mushrooms which sometimes grow from elephant droppings have magic powers. And, in one sentence, he summed up the current demise of the Sri Lankan elephants.

'Many elephants, not many people, no problem. Many people, not many elephants, big problems'.

On the question of the environment, Matara Swami says, 'Many elephants, not many people, no problem. Many people, not many elephants, big problems.'

The elephants inevitably encroach on areas of human habitation and thus begins the cycle of damaged crops, irate farmers and injured elephants.

Situations similar to this have occurred around the country with other smaller development projects. Attempts to resolve such problems have sometimes necessitated the removal of people, and other times the removal of elephants. Such attempts are usually less than satisfactory to either people or elephants.

The problems are clearly complex. Sri Lanka has an expanding human population and a growing economy. People have a right to improved living standards. Unless the country is able to compete on international markets, those standards will fall.

Some people claim that the disappearance of the Sri Lankan elephant is an inevitable price to pay for economic progress; that the elephant 'has had its day'. Others believe that workable solutions are possible and that with proper management, elephants and people can co-exist on the tiny island. And there are those who believe the survival of the elephant is crucial to the survival of Sri Lanka.

The following are just some of the diverse strategies in the management of Sri Lanka's wild elephant population.

People and elephants have lived in harmony in Sri Lanka for hundreds of years. Now, as people require more land, elephant habitat is severely diminished. All too often, this conflict results in elephant deaths.

Relocation

Many elephants have been relocated from areas of human settlements. This has met with varying degrees of success. Sometimes, relocation is simply shifting the problem to another area. Sometimes it represents only a temporary measure to a continuing problem. And often relocated elephants return. Elephants are transferred in the following ways:

Due to diminished habitat, elephants encroach into cultivated regions presenting a continued dilemma in the struggle between environmentalists and developers.

† **Elephant Drive:** This operation involves hundreds of people with thunder flashes and sticks who move in behind a herd and literally 'drive' it to new areas. It can take some days to drive the elephants to the desired location. In the process, much farmland may be destroyed and people as well as elephants may sustain injuries.

† **Tranquillisation and Transportation:** This involves darting elephants with a tranquillising gun, roping them, coaxing them onto vehicles and relocating them. Such methods, which are clearly more appropriate for single elephants than for an entire herd, are time-consuming and very expensive. They can also be traumatic for the elephant. Many elephants have died as a result of such drastic intervention. Others have simply waited until their release and then walked back to their preferred place.

Tranquillising and relocating can cause much stress to the elephant. Such methods of management have met with little success since relocated elephants frequently return to their original location.

Photos this page courtesy Rex Sellman.

Tranquillising an Elephant

At the University of Peradeniya near Kandy, Dr Kuruwita heads the tranquillisation team that frequently treats and sometimes relocates wild elephants. The team uses a morphine derivative aptly named Large Animal Immobilon. Administered via a dart gun into the rump, thigh or shoulder, the drug works within seconds. The elephant is tranquillised and falls to the ground. It is crucial that the elephant falls onto its side. A forward fall onto the lungs may result in suffocation.

Many variables influence the fall, including the presence of trees and slope of the land. If an elephant falls incorrectly, the antidote must be administered within two minutes. Elephants are never tranquillised when they are in the water.

Because wild elephants have access to a variety of plants they tend to be stronger than captive elephants. They therefore require heavier doses of immobilon to become fully tranquillised. Once the animal is immobilised, the tranquillising team must act swiftly.

To treat gunshot wounds, an incision is made and the pus removed. Large quantities of antibiotic are then injected. If an elephant is tranquillised for relocation, ropes are attached to its legs before the antidote is administered. A bulldozer or monitor (tame) elephants will coax the animal onto a truck. It is then transported to a national park, away from danger to itself or to people. Elephants captured in this manner are prone to 'Post Capture Syndrome' and may require massive doses of Vitamin E to regain muscular strength.

When an elephant is tranquillised, other elephants tend to stay close by and watch. Some try to rescue their fallen comrade. For this reason members of the tranquillisation team carry crackers to drive away the watchful elephants. In most cases the antidote, Large Animal Revivon, is administered within two hours after tranquillisation.

In 1990 Dr Kuruwita tranquillised a wild male elephant in the south of Sri Lanka. The elephant was treated for 13 gunshot wounds. High doses of antibiotic were administered and the elephant regained complete health. Three months later the same elephant required further treatment. He was suffering from fresh gunshot wounds.

The Tusker Task Force

This small group of dedicated people, initiated by Mr S. Premadasa, son of the late President, monitors the movements of tusked elephants throughout national parks and other accessible areas of elephant habitat. The data collected adds to the much-needed information on the condition and location of tuskers. Because members of the Task Force are constantly 'on watch' they are also able to report on wounded elephants and to initiate the intervention of a team with tranquillisers and antibiotics.

Managing Rogues – Shooting or Capture?

As elephant habitat continues to diminish, so more elephants are likely to become rogues. These dangerous beasts destroy life and property. Some people advocate the shooting of such animals. Others prefer capture and taming. Capture of all such animals is clearly not feasible. Therefore shooting, whether officially sanctioned or illicitly executed, will probably continue.

Breeding

In 1982 a captive breeding programme was begun at the elephant orphanage at Pinnawala and at the Colombo Zoo. In the following decade seven calves were born. According to Professor Ratnasooriya from the Department of Zoology at the University of Colombo, such an incidence of birth represents a very successful breeding programme. However, once born in captivity, an elephant will probably remain captive. To place it in the wild becomes fraught with difficulties. The most effective way to enhance breeding amongst wild elephants is to ensure sufficient undisturbed habitat.

Victims of War

Efforts to manage and increase the wild elephant population of Sri Lanka have been undermined by the protracted war in the north and the east of the island. Valuable resources that could be directed to wildlife management are consumed by the war effort.

Elephants, as well as people, are the innocent victims. No one knows exactly how many elephants have suffered a horrendous death by stepping on a land-mine, or how many have been deliberately machine-gunned because they were 'in the way'.

What is known is that the regular reports of such deaths probably represent only a fraction of the big picture. The situation is so desperate that Wilpattu National Park in the north has been totally inaccessible for some years because of land-mines.[161] People can only guess at the state of the wildlife within its unprotected boundaries.

Corridors

Establishing areas of safe passage between national parks is favoured by some environmentalists as the best solution to the complex problem. Others claim that if national parks and other areas of elephant habitat are properly maintained, corridors will not be necessary.

It is one thing to build corridors but another to maintain them. Many attempts at establishing safe passage have been thwarted by inadequate resourcing and contradictory policies of land management.

Upgrading Elephant Habitat

The enriching of elephant habitat to increase the carrying capacity requires vast resources and a well co-ordinated effort. Particular strategies for habitat enrichment may involve:

† Provision of additional tanks (watering holes)

† Extensive planting of trees, grasses and shrubs

† Prevention of soil erosion, especially around river banks.

Establishing National Parks

Approximately ten per cent of Sri Lanka is dedicated to national parks or wildlife sanctuaries. This is a significant amount of land for such a small country and reflects the value placed upon the flora and fauna. However, effective environmental maintenance and development of these protected regions are seriously wanting as government resources are directed toward other priorities such as military operations and economic development. If the ideals of elephant protection triumph, the sentiments of the inscription (overleaf) at the Yala National Park may yet be realised.

Inscription at the Entrance
to Yala National Park

Through these gates

you enter a protected area.

The animals, birds, trees, the water, the

breeze on your face and every grain of

sand, are gifts that nature has passed onto

you through your ancestors

so that you may survive.

These gifts are sacred

and should be protected.

Whisper a silent prayer as you pass

through, for protection of the wilderness

around you and ensure that what you see

and feel is passed onto the unborn

generations to come.

CONCLUSION

From our home in the hills outside Melbourne, Australia, the elephants of Sri Lanka seem very far away. Of course we have reminders. There are pictures on our walls and carvings above the fireplace. There are other reminders too. Less than three kilometres from our house is a Hindu temple dedicated to Ganesha. Two large elephant statues stand as protectors at the entrance. Sometimes we visit. And even in passing we acknowledge the elephant headed god positioned high on the temple wall. A few kilometres in another direction is a Sri Lankan Buddhist temple. There we were warmly welcomed by monks who told us colourful stories of ceremonies and elephants. Australia is a multicultural and, for the most part, a very tolerant society. For this we are grateful.

Still other reminders exist. At least once a year a circus comes to our neighbourhood. From behind a wire fence we stand and stare at the chained elephants and we remember. Returning our look they extend their trunks in our direction. Do they know that we have spent time with their cousins in a far away island?

We live on a hill and our house faces west. Sometimes we watch the clouds roll in and we think of the myths and the legends, of how the elephants once floated in the heavens, how they came to earth and became associated with rain and with good fortune. And when the moon is full we look up and we imagine that somewhere in Sri Lanka, a *perahera* is unfolding. Maybe it is a large one with up to 100 elephants; or perhaps it is a small one with only one or two. What we picture most vividly is the dignity with which the elephants execute their duties. And we know why they are revered.

Sri Lanka has become an indelible part of our lives. And we look forward to visiting whenever circumstances permit. We know that with each visit we will be warmly received by the friends we have made and the elephants we have met. But, for all our remembering and imagining, there is a sadness.

The elephants of Sri Lanka have come a long way. From the clouds to the earth; from free spirits of the land to captives for war and for work. Some are still free to roam the land. However, since we began our research, since we made our first visit, there have been more elephant deaths than births. No-one knows the exact numbers. But the elephants are clearly losing. And inevitably, so too is the ecosystem.

We hope that it is not too late. We are encouraged by the fact that there are still some elephant births in the wild. And we are moved by the people we have met who remain dedicated to ensuring a viable future for the Sri Lankan elephants. Our hope is that, in some small way, this book contributes to their efforts. Elephants are a precious gift. A better chance for survival is the least we can give back to the inimitable *Elephas maximus maximus*.

GLOSSARY

Abhramu †	In mythology the first female elephant to be created.
Airavata †	In mythology the first male elephant to be created.
Ankus	A two metre stick with a point and hook at one end, used to goad an elephant.
Anuradhapura	One of the ancient cities. Situated in north-central Sri Lanka, it now forms part of the area known as the cultural triangle. It was close to here that Buddhism was introduced to Sri Lanka.
Ath-gala	Sinhalese term for kraal, a method of capturing large numbers of elephants by the use of a stockade.
Basnayaka Nilame	Chief lay custodian of a temple or shrine to a deity.
Caste	The ancient texts categorise elephants into castes according to their attributes.
Chaddanta	An elephant of high caste and noble breed. See caste above.
Dagaba †	Domed religious edifice housing relics, usually for the Buddha.
Decoy elephant	Tame elephant used to lure wild elephants for capture.
Devale	Shrine or temple of a deity.
Dig-gajas	In mythology, the elephants which support the universe.
Disawe	Governor of a district.
Diyawadana Nilame	Lay custodian of the Temple of the Sacred Tooth Relic in Kandy.
Esala Mangalle	Festival held at the time of the July/August full moon.
Esala †	Time of the July/August full moon.
Gaja Sastra	Ancient text on the science of elephants written about 600 – 500 BC.
Gajanayake Nilame	In the time of the Sinhalese kings this person was the custodian of the elephant stables. Currently this position is largely ceremonial at the processions where elephants participate.
Ganesha	The elephant headed god.
Ganga	River.
Hatthalhaka	Elephant post.
Hatthalhaka-vihara	The convent built near where the state elephant grazed.
Hatthipakara	Wall of carved elephants.
Hiranyagarbha	In mythology, the egg from which the sun god and the original elephants were created.
Howdah	Platform with canopy for elephant's back.
Indra	God of rain.
Jataka	Stories of the previous births of the Buddha.
Kandula	Elephant belonging to the King Dutugemunu honoured and remembered for his courage in war.
Kataragama	Town in the south east of Sri Lanka significant to Hindus, Buddhists and Muslims. The deity of this area is Skanda, also known as Murugan.
Kataragama god	The deity of the area of Kataragama. Also known as Skanda or Murugan.
Kovil	Shrine to a deity.
Kraal	Enclosure or stockade used to capture large numbers of elephants.
Mahabharata	Indian epic composed around 1,000 BC, based on Vedic myths and describing events in approximately 1,400 to 1,300 BC.
Mahavamsa	Ancient chronicle depicting the history of the Sinhalese people.
Mahout	Elephant keeper.
Maligawa Tusker	A generic term for the tusked elephant which carries the relics of the Buddha in the Kandy procession. This term is also used specifically to refer to the elephant Raja, which undertook this task for almost 50 years.
Matangalila	Ancient text – *The Playful Treatise on Elephants.*
Monitor elephant	Tame elephant used to control and subdue new captive elephants.
Navam	The time during January/February which commemorates several events in Buddhist history including the first Buddhist Council.
Nibbana	The attaining of enlightenment (also known as Nirvana).
Nila	Nerve points on the elephant which may be goaded by the keeper to discipline or direct an elephant.

GLOSSARY

Nilame	Chieftain.
Nirvana	As per Nibbana.
Paddy	Rice in the husk. Paddy field – the rice field.
Padma	Lotus. A name given to the goddess Lotus also known as Sri Lakshmi.
Panniker	Traditional elephant trapper.
Pawada	The white cloth upon which the elephant that carries the relics of the Buddha walks.
Perahera	Procession often including elephants.
Peramune Rala	The dignitary who leads the procession.
Poson	Time of year, May/June, when the arrival of Buddhism to Sri Lanka is celebrated.
Puja	Offering.
Raja-Kariya	Service to the royal household.
Ramayana	Indian epic composed about 1,000 BC, depicting the war between India and Ceylon.
Relics	Corporeal remains and belongings of a revered person, preserved and revered after death.
Saman	Deity of the Sri Pada region in south-west Sri Lanka.
Saman (Holy melodies)	Chanted by the creator Brahma as the original elephants came into being.
Sandakada-pahana	Moonstone. Carved stone at the entrance to many temples.
Sarong	Garment of long cloth wrapped around the body and tucked at waist.
Sri Lakshmi	Goddess of abundance and fertility, known also as goddess Lotus and Padma.
Sri Dalada Maligawa	Temple of the Sacred Tooth Relic in Kandy.
Sumanakuta	The area of Sri Pada – region of the deity Saman.
Tank	Ancient human construction similar to a vast lake or reservoir.
Thera, Theri	Honorific titles for monk and nun respectively.
Thupa	Domed edifice enshrining relics of the Buddha.
Tusker	Elephant with tusks.
Vishnu	Regarded as guardian deity of Sri Lanka and also of Buddhism on the island.
Walige Kota	Short tailed elephant.

Spellings †

Many different spellings exist for some of the terms used in this book. The spellings adopted throughout the book are those in most frequent usage. Most variations involve the use of accents. For those terms with greater variations, alternatives are listed here.

Atha	Etha, Ätha
Dadimunda	Dädimunda, Daedimundā
Dutugemunu	Dutthagāmani
Esala	Äsala
Nibbana	Nirvāna
Perahera	Perahära
Vesak	Wesak
Walawwa	Walawe

ENDNOTES

1. Difference of opinion exists over the specific dates of events. For the purposes of this book we have used Wimalaratne, K.D.G. 1988, *Directory of Dates and Events Sri Lanka (Ceylon) (543 BC - 1984 AD)*.
2. Geiger, p. 172.
3. For further information on species differentiation, refer to the writings of Deraniyagala and Shoshani.
4. *Matangalila*, in Zimmer, 1972, pp. 103-5.
5. Williams, p. 8.
6. (i) *Gaja Sastra*, (ii) Gupta, p. 7.
7. *Gaja Sastra*.
8. Navarane, p. 51.
9. *The Mahabharata*, in Zimmer, 1972, pp. 92, 105-6.
10. Zimmer, 1972, p. 107.
11. Harischandra, pp. 48-9.
12. Zimmer, 1955, vol. 1, p. 161.
13. Zimmer, 1955, vol. 1, p. 161.
14. De Silva, p. 234.
15. Zimmer, 1972, pp. 90-102.
16. From the Ancient Text, *Hastyayurveda*, in Zimmer, 1972, p. 108.
17. Zimmer, 1972, pp. 108-9.
18. Wijesekera, Part I, p. 8.
19. Ratnapala, p. 119.
20. It is not suggested that elephants would have been killed for this purpose.
21. From the Jatakas and also Lefmann, S. (ed.) 1908, *Lalitavistara*, in Gupta, pp. 31-32.
22. Ions, p. 129.
23. Weinman, A. 'Elephants and Their Ways', *Loris*, Dec. 1951, p. 300.
24. *Vessantara-Jataka* no. 547, Book XXII, vol. VI, in Cowell, pp. 246-305.
25. *Kulavaka-Jataka*, no. 31, Book 1, vol. 1, in Cowell, pp. 76-81.
26. *Cullahamsa-Jataka*, no. 533, Book XXI, vol. V, in Cowell, pp. 175-186.
27. *Chaddanta-Jataka*, no. 514, Book XVI, vol. V, in Cowell, pp. 20-30.
28. 'The Monks of Kosamba', in Dharmasena Thera, pp. 112-121.
29. The Dhammapada, pp. 342-353.
30. 'Lesser Discourse on the Simile of the Elephants Footprint', in Horner, pp. 220-230.
31. Zimmer, 1955, vol. 1, p. 46.
32. Williams, p. 162
33. De Silva, p. 64.
34. Geiger, p. 119.
35. Geiger, p. 119.
36. Geiger, p. 164.
37. Geiger, p. 172.
38. Geiger, p. 175.
39. Geiger, p. 176.
40. Geiger, p. 170.
41. Geiger, p. 248.
42. Geiger, p. 248.
43. Geiger, p. 248.
44. Geiger, p. 249.
45. Invocation to the deity Saman, in Obeyesekere, p. 94.
46. Aksland, p. 41.
47. Karunakaran, p. 52.
48. Lal, p. 20.
49. Deraniyagala, p. 137.
50. However, elephant testicles are internal.
51. Tennent, 1977, p. 779.
52. Madugalle, p. 65.
53. This information was compiled from the ancient texts, *Maha Gaja Lakshana Sangrahava, Gajayoga Satakaya, Gajatu Lakshanaya*, and *Hasti Lakshana Vidyava*. These texts are translated in Deraniyagala, pp. 135-139.
54. Shoshani, p. 66.
55. (i) Shoshani, p. 46. (ii) We gained further information on this point in conversation with Dr Jeheskel Shoshani in New York, Jan. 1994.
56. Deraniyagala, p. 48.
57. Deraniyagala, p.9.
58. From the Ancient Text, *Atunge Lakshana*, in Deraniyagala, pp. 137-138.
59. Schneck, p. 19.
60. From the Ancient Text, *Atunge Lakshana*, in Deraniyagala, pp. 137-138.
61. Sukumar, p. 81.
62. From the Ancient Text, *Atunge Lakshana*, in Deraniyagala pp. 137-139.
63. Deraniyagala, p. 138.
64. (i) Deraniyagala, p. 61. (ii) Delort p. 24.
65. Deraniyagala, p. 138.
66. Information provided by Dr Brendon Gooneratne, Aug. 1994.
67. Deraniyagala, p. 136.
68. Deraniyagala, p. 137.
69. Chadwick, p. 77.
70. Carrington, p. 52.
71. Olivier, p. 269.
72. McKay, pp. 74-79.
73. Tennent, 1977, pp. 794-795.
74. Tennent, 1977, p. 786.
75. Redmond, 1990, p. 12.
76. Moss, p. 128.
77. Moss, p. 125.
78. McKay, p. 67.
79. Moss, p. 313.
80. Moss, p. 314.
81. McKay, p. 65.
82. Redmond, 1990, p. 28.
83. Chadwick, pp. 77-78.
84. Tennent, 1977, p. 778.
85. Tennent, 1977, p. 778.
86. Tennent, 1977, p. 810.
87. Tennent, 1977, p. 775.
88. Redmond, 1993, p. 60.
89. Shoshani, p. 229.
90. Redmond, 1993, p. 39.
91. *Matangalila*, in McKay, p. 1.
92. *Ramayana*, in Shoshani, p. 82.
93. Elapata, S.A.I. 'The Sexual Behaviour of Wild Elephants in Ceylon', *Loris*, Jun. 1969, p. 247 (Jubilee Issue).
94. Udugama, p. 50.
95. *Loris*, Sep. 1951.
96. Shoshani, p. 80. According to Shoshani the Jacobson's organ functions to process chemical cues and transfer information to the brain.
97. Elapata, S.A.I. 'The Sexual Behaviour of Wild Elephants in Ceylon', *Loris* Jun. 1969, pp. 246 -247.
98. Elapata, S. Junior, 'Mating of Elephants in Captivity', *Loris*, Jun. 1969, p. 256.
99. Ratnasooriya, 1990, p. 56.
100. Deraniyagala, p. 60.
101. Moss, p. 270.
102. Douglas-Hamilton, p. 239.
103. Schneck, p. 102.
104. From 'Arabian Night's Entertainment', in Tennent, p. 875.
105. Tennent, 1977, p. 875.
106. As early as the third century AD sophisticated irrigation systems were established. Such systems comprised huge tanks (artificial lakes) which stored and regulated supply of water. These tanks, which sustained flourishing cultures, were further developed in the 12th century. Some of the original tanks are still in use today.
107. Sirr, vol. I, p. 188.
108. As told to us in an interview in Melbourne with Venerable Davuldena Nanissara Thero, High Priest and Chief Incumbent at Sri Vidya Vijaya Aramaya, Taiwan, Apr. 1991.
109. Tennent, 1977, p. 770.
110. Deraniyagala, p. 45.
111. Tennent, 1977, p. 770.
112. Deraniyagala, p. 68.
113. Somanader, S.V.O. 'Noosing Ceylon's Wild Elephants', *Ceylon Today*, Jul. 1957, p. 21.
114. Jayasekera, A. 'How to Catch an Elephant', first published in *Times*, 14 Sep. 1960, and reprinted in *Loris*, Dec. 1964, pp. 78-79.
115. Clark, p. 26.
116. Mohideen, S. *The Island*, Jul. 17 1992.
117. *Ramayana*, in Eltringham, p. 136.
118. Tennent, 1977, p. 843.
119. Tennent, 1977, p. 836.
120. Tennent, 1977, p. 849.
121. Deraniyagala, p. 59.
122. Deraniyagala, p. 60.
123. Tennent, 1977, p. 849.
124. Anthonisz, S. (trans.) *Diary of the Occurrences During the Tour of Gerrit de Heere, Governor of Ceylon from Colombo to Jaffna, July 9 to September 3, 1697*, Government Printer, Ceylon, 1914.
125. Deraniyagala, p. 60.
126. Hockin, J. 'The Last Kraal', first published 1950, reprinted in *Loris*, Jun. 1951, pp. 247-248.
127. Tammitta, R.B. Asst Editor, *Times* in *The Island*, 17-11-85.
128. Delort, p. 87.
129. Baker, p. 79.
130. Bulner, 10-10-1971, p. 3.
131. (i) Bulner, (ii) Mr Sam Mottau, interview, Jul. 1991.
132. Weinman, A. 'The Vanishing Herd', in *Loris*, Dec. 1964, pp. 75-76.
133. 'Death of a Wildlife Photographer', in *Loris*, Dec. 1951, pp. 293-295.
134. Tennent, 1977, p. 794.
135. Baker, p. 13.
136. Baker, p. 13.
137. Deraniyagala, p. 144.
138. From the Ancient Text, *Gaja Yogaratnaya*, quoted in Deraniyagala, p. 145.
139. Knox, in Ludowyk, p. 180.
140. Deraniyagala, p. 142.
141. Deraniyagala, p. 140.
142. *Loris*, Jun. 1964.
143. Deraniyagala, pp. 146-147.
144. Deraniyagala, pp. 69-70.
145. Deraniyagala, p. 140.
146. This story was originally published in the *Observer*, 26 Dec. 1963 and later in *Loris*, Jun. 1964, p. 61.
147. Weinman, A. 1951, 'Elephants and Their Ways' in *Loris*, Dec. p. 297.
148. *Vessantara-Jataka*, no. 547, Book XXII, vol. VI, in Cowell, pp. 246-305.
149. From information supplied by Brothers Peter and Justin, Community of the Many Names of God, Llanpumsaint, Wales, Jan. 1993.
150. De Silva, p. 234.
151. De Silva, p. 234.
152. Seneviratna, p. 66.
153. (i) Madugalle.
(ii) We are also grateful to Mr Neranjan Wijeyeratne, Lay Custodian to the Temple of the Sacred Tooth Relic, for information supplied.
154. From Texts of the Pahan Pujava: *Offering of Lights*, in Obeyesekere, p. 80.
155. Obeyesekere, p. 472.
156. De Silva, pp. 219-223.
157. Obeyesekere, p. 321.
158. Eltringham, in Shoshani, p. 127.
159. Nicholas, C.W. 1952, 'The Present Status of the Ceylon Elephant', *Ceylon Today*, I, 1 Sep. 1952, in Gooneratne, B.W.M., p. 151.
160. Molamure, A.H.E. 'As to the Good and Bad Points of the Elephants, their Marks Auspicious and Inauspicious', in *Loris*, Jun. 1969, p. 272.
161. Dr S. Kotagama, Former Head of Department of Wildlife Conservation, provided this information during an interview in Jan. 1993.

SELECT BIBLIOGRAPHY

Aksland, M. 1990, *The Sacred Footprint*, YETI Consult, Oslo.

Baker, S.W. 1983 (1855), *Eight Years in Ceylon*, 3rd edn, Tisara Press, Sri Lanka.

Brohier, R.L. 1973, *Discovering Ceylon*, Lake House Investments, Colombo.

Brohier, R.L. 1981, *Seeing Ceylon*, Lake House Investments, Colombo.

Bulner, J.J. 1971, 'Excerpts from Elephant Country', *Observer*, Colombo, Sep.-Oct.

Carrington, R. 1958, *Elephants, a Short Account of their Natural History, Evolution and Influence on Mankind*, Chatto & Windus, London.

Carter, R.C. & Palihawadana, M. 1987, *The Dhammapada*, Oxford University Press, New York.

Chadwick, D.H. 1992, *The Fate of the Elephant*, Viking, London.

Clark, A. 1971 (1901), *Sport in the Low-Country of Ceylon*, 2nd edn, Tisara Prakasakayo, Ceylon.

Cordiner, J. 1983 (1807), *A Description of Ceylon*, 2nd edn, 2 vols, Tisara Press, Sri Lanka.

Cowell, E.B. (ed.) 1969, *The Jataka, or Stories of the Buddha's Former Births*, 6 vols, published for the Pali Text Society by Luzac & Company Ltd, London.

De Silva, L. 1974, *Buddhism, Beliefs and Practices in Sri Lanka*, Sioll School of Technology, Battaramulla.

De Silva, R.K. 1985, *Early Prints of Ceylon (Sri Lanka) 1800 – 1900*, Serendib Publications, London.

De Silva, R.K. & Beumer, W.G.M. 1988, *Illustrations and Views of Dutch Ceylon 1602 – 1796*, Serendib Publications, London.

De Lanerolle, N. 1985, *A Reign of Ten Kings*, Ceylon Tourist Board, Colombo.

Delort, R. 1990, *The Life and Lore of the Elephant*, Thames & Hudson, London.

Department of Wildlife Conservation, 1990, *Proceedings of the Seminar on the Conservation Plan for Elephants of Sri Lanka*, Sri Lanka.

Deraniyagala, P.E.P. 1955, *Some Extinct Elephants, their Relatives and the Two Living Species*, Ceylon National Museums, Ceylon.

Dharmadasa, K.N.O. & De A. Samarasinghe, S.W.R. 1990, *The Vanishing Aborigines*, Vikas Publishing House Pvt Ltd, New Delhi, in assoc. with NORAD & International Centre for Ethnic Studies.

Dharmasena Thera 1991, *Jewels of the Doctrine*, trans. R. Obeyesekere, State University of New York Press, Albany.

Douglas-Hamilton, Iain & Oria 1975, *Among the Elephants*, Book Club Associates, London.

Eltringham, S.K. 1991, *The Illustrated Encyclopedia of Elephants*, Salamander Books, New York.

Freeman, D. 1980, *Elephants, The Vanishing Giants*, A.P. Publishing, A Bison Book, London.

Ghavacharyar, V.V. (ed.) (unpub. attributed to Palakapya, 600-500 BC) 1927, *Gaja Sastra, Science of Elephants*, available at Museum Library, Colombo.

Geiger, W. (trans.) 1950 (1912), *The Mahavamsa or The Great Chronicle of Ceylon*, The Ceylon Government Information Department, Colombo.

Gombrich, R. & Obeyesekere, G. 1990, *Buddhism Transformed, Religious Change in Sri Lanka*, Motilal Banarsidass Publishers Pvt Ltd, Delhi.

Gooneratne, B.W.M. 1967, 'The Ceylon Elephant, *Elephas maximus zeylanicus*: its decimation and fight for survival', *Ceylon Journal of Historical and Social Studies*, 10, pp. 149-160.

Gupta, S.K. 1983, *Elephant in Indian Art and Mythology*, Abhinav Publications, New Delhi.

Harishchandra, B.W. 1985, *The Sacred City of Anuradhapura*, Asian Educational Services, New Delhi.

Hennessy, D.J.G. 1967, *The Lord of the Jungle*, Robert Hale Ltd, London.

Horner, I.B. 1954, 'Lesser Discourse on the Simile of the Elephant's Footprint' in *The Collection of the Middle Length Sayings*, vol. I, published for the Pali Text Society by Luzac & Company Ltd, London.

Ions, V. 1967, *Indian Mythology*, Hamlyn, London.

Ishwaran, N. 1981, 'Comparative Study of Asiatic Elephant *Elephas maximus* populations in Gal Oya, Sri Lanka' *Biological Conservation 21*, pp. 303-313.

Ishwaran, N. 1983, 'Elephant and Woody-Plant Relationships in Gal Oya, Sri Lanka' *Biological Conservation 26*, pp. 255-270.

Jayewardene, J. 1994, *The Elephant in Sri Lanka*, (dist. in Sri Lanka by Wildlife Heritage Trust, Colombo).

Karunakaran, R. 1992, *The Riddle of Ganesha*, Book Quest, Bombay.

Kunkel, R. 1982, *Elephants*, Harry N. Abradale Press, New York.

Lal, L. 1991, *Ganesha, Beyond the Form*, IBI Publishers Pvt Ltd, Bombay.

SELECT BIBLIOGRAPHY

Loris, The Journal of the Wildlife and Nature Protection Society of Sri Lanka.

Ludowyk, E.F.C. 1985, *The Story of Ceylon*, Navrang, New Delhi.

Madugalle, S.J. 1989, *Raja, The Sri Dalada Maligawa Tusker*, Ministry of Education, Cultural Affairs and Information, Colombo.

McKay, G.M. 1973, 'Behaviour and Ecology of the Asiatic Elephant in Southeastern Ceylon' *Smithsonian Contributions to Zoology*, Number 125, Smithsonian Institution Press, Washington.

Moss, C. 1988, *Elephant Memories*, Fontana Collins, Glasgow.

Murray, N. 1976, *The Love of Elephants*, Octopus Books Limited, London.

Naravane, V.S. 1965, *The Elephant and the Lotus*, Asia Publishing House, London.

Obeyesekere, G. 1984, *The Cult of the Goddess Pattini*, Motilal Banarsidass, Delhi.

Olivier, R.C.D. 1978, On the Ecology of the Asian Elephant *Elephas maximus* Linn, PhD thesis, Cambridge University.

Olivier, R.C.D. 1979, 'The Case of the Missing Pachyderms' *Animal Kingdom*, Oct./Nov. vol. 82, no. 5, pp. 6-12.

Orenstein, R. (ed.) 1991, *Elephants, Saving the Gentle Giants*, Bloomsbury Publishing, London.

Parker, H. 1984 (1909), *Ancient Ceylon*, 2nd edn, Asian Educational Services, New Delhi.

Phillips, W.W.A. 1980, *Manual of the Mammals of Sri Lanka*, 2nd edn, Wildlife and Nature Protection Society of Sri Lanka.

Ratnapala, N. 1991, *Folklore of Sri Lanka*, State Printing Corporation, Sri Lanka.

Ratnasooriya, W.D. 1990, 'The Vanishing Elephant', *Proceedings of the Forty-sixth Annual Session*, Sri Lanka Association for the Advancement of Science, Colombo, Dec.

Redmond, I. 1990, *The Elephant Book*, Walker Books, London.

Redmond, I. 1993, *Elephant*, Harper Collins, Australia.

Santiapillai, C., Chambers, M.R. & Ishwaran, N. 1984, 'Aspects of the Ecology of the Asian Elephant *Elephas maximus* L. in the Ruhuna National Park, Sri Lanka' *Biological Conservation, 29*, pp. 47-61.

Schneck, M. 1991, *Elephants, Gentle Giants of Africa and Asia*, Todtri, New York.

Seneviratna, A. 1990, *Buddhist Rituals and Ceremonies, Temple of the Sacred Tooth Relic in Sri Lanka*, Department of Cultural Affairs, Government of Sri Lanka.

Seneviratne, M. 1979, *Some Mahavamsa Places*, Lake House Investments Ltd, Colombo.

Shastra, T. (ed.) 1910, Matangalila, Trivandum, Sanskrit Series, no. X, in Zimmer, H. 1972, *Myths and Symbols in Indian Art and Civilisation*, ed. J. Campbell, Bollingen Series VI, Princeton University Press, Princeton, N.J. pp. 103-5.

Shoshani, J. (ed.) 1992, *Elephants, Majestic Creatures of the Wild*, Weldon Owen, Sydney.

Sirr, H.C. 1850, *Ceylon and the Cingalese*, 2 vols, William Shoberl, London.

Sukumar, R. 1989, *The Asian Elephant, Ecology and Management*, Cambridge University Press, Cambridge.

Tennent, J.E. 1977 (1859), *Ceylon*, vol. 2, 6th edn, Tisara, Sri Lanka.

Tennent, J.E. 1867, *The Wild Elephant and the Method of Capturing and Taming it in Ceylon*, Longmans, Green & Co., London.

Udugama, S. 1983, *Sri Lanka – From Legend and History*, Niloo Bhatt, Colombo.

Van Rhee, T. 1915, *Memoir for his Successor Gerrit de Heere, 1697*, Government Printer, Ceylon.

Vaughan-Whitehead, P. 1969, 'End of an Era: Ceylon's Elephants replaced by Tractors' an F.O.A. Feature, *Commonwealth Forestry Review,* vol. 48(4), no. 138, Dec.

Weerakoon, R. 1985, *Sri Lanka's Mythology*, Samayawardhana-Colombo.

Wijesekera, N. 1987, *Deities and Demons, Magic and Masks*, Parts 1 & 2, Gunasena, Colombo.

Williams, H. 1989, *Sacred Elephant*, Jonathan Cape, London.

Williams, J.H. 1951, *Elephant Bill*, Reprint Society of London, London.

Wimalaratne, K.D.G. 1988, *Directory of Events, Sri Lanka (Ceylon) (543BC – 1984AD)*, Trumpet Publishers Pvt Ltd, Colombo.

Woolf, L. 1983, *Diaries in Ceylon 1908 – 1911*, 2nd edn, Tisara Prakasakayo Ltd, Sri Lanka.

Zimmer, H. 1955, *The Art of Indian Asia: Its Mythology and Transformations*, 2 vols, completed and ed. J. Campbell, Pantheon Books, New York.

Zimmer, H. 1972, *Myths and Symbols in Indian Art and Civilisation*, ed. J. Campbell, Princeton University Press, Princeton, N. J.

INDEX

INDEX

INDEX

END